Guide to Desktop Linux in 2025

What Most of Your Penguin Friends Won't Tell You

James North

Guide to Desktop Linux in 2025

What Most of Your Penguin Friends Won't Tell You

www.EvolveGlobalPublishing.com

Guide to Desktop Linux in 2025: *What Most of Your Penguin Friends Won't Tell You*

1st Edition: 2025 v1.1

eBook

ASIN: B0DRZ9MGQS
ISBN: 978-1-923223-65-3

Paperback

Ingram Spark Paperback ISBN: 978-1-923223-66-0
Amazon Paperback ISBN: 978-1-923223-67-7
Lulu Paperback ISBN: 978-1-923223-68-4

Hardcover

Ingram Spark Hardcover ISBN: 978-1-923223-69-1

CONTACT THE AUTHOR:

Business Name: EVOLVE SYSTEMS GROUP PTY LTD
Author Website: www.jamesnorth.net
Main Website: www.EvolveGlobalPublishing.com
Email: books@vncompat.org

Table of Contents

About This Book's Copyright

If you ask me for permission, I may be willing to waive some of these conditions. See the **Contact me if you want to sell derivative work, like translations** section for more information.

See the end of the book for the full legalcode of the license.

Won't you make less money by releasing your books under a Creative Commons License?

Probably, but I'd prefer someone read my books for free than not at all. Besides, you should be able to share your books with your friends and family, regardless of whether it's physical or digital.

No DRM. Ever.

DRM, or Digital Rights Management, is a technological measure which prevents customers from copying or accessing a digital version of something (e.g. a book, a game, or software) in ways the copyright holder does not approve of. It allows copyright holders to take away what you've paid for at any time, for any reason.

I don't like DRM. I don't buy books encumbered with DRM. I don't want to encumber my work with DRM, either. You paid for this book; you should be free to do whatever the hell you want with it—with the exception of reselling digital versions.

If you somehow ended up with a DRM-encumbered version of this book, you can access a DRM-free copy from this link: https://jamesnorth.net/s/dlg2025

Share this book!

If you liked this book, please share it.

Give it to a friend, a colleague, or even an enemy. I'm not picky. Make your students read it. If you want to become an audiobook narrator, read this book and post it on Librivox. Translate it for your friends if you like, and contact me if you want to sell the translation.

If you want to redistribute this book, I recommend using BitTorrent. It's a peer-to-peer protocol that transfers content not from one central server, but from multiple 'seeders' who have part or all of the file. It is less costly to run, and it has checksums built-in to ensure the integrity of the file. It's superior to HTTPS in many ways, but is particularly good for those with a slow internet connection. You can continue the download at any time from where you left off, because the file is split into many small parts.

The best part? After you've transferred 100% of the files to someone else, they can become a seed. That means you don't need to give up any more of your bandwidth after serving the first person. Assuming they're decent enough to pass the favour on, anyway.

Creating a new torrent is easy with free software clients like qBittorrent. The hardest part of this process is finding a good public tracker on which to announce the file. Even suggesting public trackers which are known to disseminate copyrighted content without permission from the author is enough to land you in jail in some countries, so the only one I can recommend is Internet Archive. They're known for being very careful about what content they redistribute. If you are savvy, you can setup your own torrent tracker with free software—but that rather defeats the purpose of saving costs, doesn't it?

The cover is copyrighted.

I reserve the rights to the cover for this book. Please don't use it without my permission. Come up with your own cover if you want to display this book for free (NonCommercial uses only, remember?) somewhere. You need to attribute me as the author of the book.

Contact me if you want to sell derivative work, like translations.

While I don't want anyone selling an unaltered copy of my work, I'm very happy to let authors sell work based on my writing. I'm also super happy to hear about someone translating my work. Please contact me at books@vncompat.org with a copy of your work asking for permission to sell it. I will most likely say yes. You are required to license your work under CC-BY NC-SA.

If I give you permission to sell it, I want a portion of the royalties. The standard amount of royalties you need to give me is 10%.

If you're concerned I won't allow you to sell your work after you put all the effort in, send me an outline of your work so I can okay it early into the project.

I would prefer the copy of your work to be in one of these formats:

- Plain Text
- Markdown
- EPUB

I would prefer you didn't send me a PDF file. I won't open any .doc, .docx, or .odt files sent to me.

I choose ShareAlike because I don't want authors creating works other authors can't use, but more importantly, works that can't be freely redistributed. Note also that Creative Commons Licenses prohibit recipients of your book from encumbering your work with DRM: https://creativecommons.org/faq/#is-creative-commons-involved-in-digital-rights-management-drm

Thanks for reading my book!

Dedication

This book is dedicated to my grandfather, Charles McLeod, who was a lifelong fan of penguins and had a mind toward solving problems himself. I always admired his fixation on self-reliance at all costs, and it was the quality I most wanted to emulate growing up. That, and his great sense of humour.

Part 1

Getting Started With Desktop Linux

Chapter 01: What is Linux, and Why Use it on Your Desktop?

Welcome to my Desktop Linux Guide, 2025 Edition! The very first edition, in fact. This is a book about the Linux Desktop written for two very different readers, divided loosely into two Parts. The first Part is for readers new to desktop Linux, who are curious what it's all about, and want to know how to get into it. The second Part is for readers already familiar with desktop Linux who want to know about its current state and where it's headed. I have quite a few opinions about this after obsessively learning everything there is to know about the Linux desktop for the past few years.[1]

While there are many books out there about learning how to use Linux on the server, there aren't nearly as many up-to-date books[2] about the Linux Desktop. There's good reason for that—while most companies use Linux for their servers, most everyday people have never heard of it.

And that's a shame! The Linux Desktop, while perennially imperfect, has a lot to offer. Depending on who you are sand what you use computers for, you might even decide to switch to Linux full-time. It might become an all-consuming passion that takes over your life, and on the rare occasion you're spotted outside, it is with a Freewear T-Shirt, because somehow your wardrobe is now entirely composed of clothing with pictures of penguins, feet, and obscure tech memes.

Or it might not be for you at all, and that's fine too. That's what I'm here to help you find out: what's all the Linux fuss about?

What is Linux, anyway?

It all started a long time ago, in 1991…

Wait, maybe it was in 1983?

The history of Linux (and GNU) is not important at this very moment. It is long and of great personal interest to me, but not yet to you, I suspect.

Linux is an **Operating System**—but what does that mean? Your laptop, desktop computer, and your phone all need an operating system to function, and yet it is not meant to be seen, so most people never think about operating systems. People don't use operating systems; they use apps like Google Chrome and Photoshop.

An operating system's job is to give programs access to your machine, and give you access to the programs.

When Photoshop wants to save a file to your machine's hard drive, it needs to ask the operating system to do that. When you press a key down on your keyboard, the keyboard sends a signal to the operating system that you've pressed a key, which then tells Google Chrome you've pressed a key. Chrome, knowing you're currently focused on the search bar, inserts the key you pressed into the search bar. You can think of an operating system as a middle man.

An operating system has a long list of responsibilities, and while the way each handles its responsibilities differs, they all fulfill the same purpose: being the control center at which the user operates the system. At this poin, you may be starting to wonder why it matters at all what operating system you choose, if they all do the same thing in the end.

As it turns out, the way in which operating systems handle (or shirk) their responsibilities can matter a great deal.

The two most popular desktop operating systems are Windows, which you'll find on most computers, and macOS, which you will only find on Apple devices. And then there's Linux...which I'll talk about shortly.

How Microsoft Windows handles its responsibilities

Windows is the most popular desktop operating system in the world. Your computer probably came with it. And despite the operating system's goal to be unseen and its presence only felt, if you use Windows, you're likely cognizant of it. Windows does a great job of getting you into whatever program you need to use and is generally reliable; a tribute to its long history as a business workhorse. It is compatible with almost every program because of how widely used it is. It's great for playing video games, video production, and pretty much anything else you need to do.

However, it has a reputation for taking advantage of its authority, especially in its most recent iterations. System notifications are used for informing the user of updates or perhaps of a new message someone sent you in your chat program. Windows uses the same space to advertise services like OneDrive and Xbox to you.

The Start menu lists all the programs installed on your computer, which you will open to find and start those programs. Windows dedicates a portion of the menu to advertising sponsored programs or even its own apps, like Microsoft 365 and Microsoft Teams.

If you open Microsoft Edge, the default web browser on Windows, and search for Google Chrome using Microsoft's search engine, you'll be confronted with banners begging you not to install Chrome, as you already have a great browser installed.

In File Explorer, where you manage all your files, you'll get more advertisements for OneDrive. On Windows 11, you may even be tricked into using it because of how the interface is designed.

When you boot into Windows for the first time, it presents you with a list of switches, each about sharing your data with Microsoft and its partners so it can improve Windows or profit from you. These are toggled on by default. Toggling them all off does not stop Windows from extracting your data once you're in the desktop, as Microsoft has many more ways of making you talk, as it were.

This is only a small slice of the Windows experience. This is what you'll see in your first hour of using the operating system. Don't assume Microsoft will stop here; their objective is to wear you down eventually.

It is clear that Microsoft's priority is to coax you into using the operating system in a way that takes advantage of all their other products and services and makes them more money, no matter how obtrusive it needs to be. While Windows fulfills its responsibilities, it seizes every opportunity to take advantage of you.

How Apple's macOS handles its responsibilities

If you bought an Apple computer like a Macbook or an iMac, you're using macOS. While Windows is a commercial product you can buy from Microsoft and install on your computer, macOS is a bundle deal. It's included with Apple computers for free. While not every company makes software for Macs, most of the important ones do. You'll be able to do most of the things you want to do with a computer, with a single major exception.

When you setup the computer for the first time, it prompts you to sign in with your Apple ID, which you will be familiar with if you already own an iPhone. If not, don't worry—you can create an Apple ID immediately. This is quickly followed by a prompt to setup Apple Pay, which makes it easier for you to pay for purchases in Safari, Apple's browser, or the App Store.

Once you've launched into the desktop, you will be presented with a string of icons. These are the pre-installed apps on your Mac. These include Messages, which you can use to continue conversations you've had on your iPhone, and Apple Music, which syncs all your music from your iPhone. There's also the Apple TV app, where you can watch all the shows you've purchased on your Apple TV.

Unlike Windows, you will never be bugged about Apple's products and services in their notifications. The system is designed to work great if you use all of Apple's products and services, which are right there, but while it acts like a gravity distortion field pulling you in, you can use whatever apps and services you want, and Apple will never beg you to use theirs.

Apple's priority is for you to have a great experience with their products. They can't afford to push you around like Windows does because their market share isn't nearly as high. And besides, they know they get more evangelical users when users choose Apple's products instead of being strong-armed. macOS is, however, designed to be used in a specific way. If you don't like the way something works, you might be able to change it, but even then you may not like any of the other options. This philosophy was immortalised over a decade ago when a customer was experiencing a problem with their iPhone failing to get an internet connection, and Apple's response was simply, "you're holding it wrong."

It takes years, sometimes decades for Apple to change their mind about certain design choices. It took 41 years for macOS to gain a feature both Windows and Linux have had for many, many years: window snapping. This feature is considered basic by a large number of users, but Apple did not consider it important, so they didn't implement it for almost half a century. Chances are, there are other things you don't like about macOS but can't change. With Linux, you get a lot more options.

And while Apple won't beg you to choose their products, they won't make any effort to support alternatives in most cases. They won't stop you, but they won't help you. If you've got an Android phone instead of an Apple phone and you want to transfer files, good luck to you. The more Apple products you own, the better the experience is. If your only Apple product is a Mac, the experience is good, but not insanely great. The implication is clear, but not obtrusive in the same way as Windows is.

Macs are not great for playing video games either. Apple has neglected to support the graphics technology game developers rely on across all platforms—called OpenGL and Vulkan—as well as Linux or Windows, and has left it to rot. Like with much of Apple's operating system, it is theirs; its their way or the highway. There is a new technology that game developers must go out of their way to support in order to offer first-class support for macOS—called Metal. For this reason, Linux has a higher market share on Steam, the biggest desktop gaming platform.[3]

Finally, Apple hardware comes at a premium. You can install Linux on a toaster (and companies do); if you don't have the money for an Apple computer and you don't care for Windows, you could always buy a computer that comes with Windows and replace it with Linux.

How Linux handles its responsibilities

Linux, in most parts of the world, is something you choose. Its users needed to fight their computer to choose Linux, and so are naturally protective of it. And so there is a tendency to ignore problems or simply forget to mention them to other people whenever the topic of Linux spontaneously comes up in day-to-day conversation. The operating system is not as perfect as you may have been led to believe, but that doesn't mean you can't do real work on it, or have real fun with it.

Anyone can make a **Linux distribution**, which is another word for a Linux-based operating system. That means it could be backed by a multinational corporation, or a random guy who really likes Hannah Montana.[4]

In most cases, Linux distributions make no effort to advertise to you because they have nothing to sell. There are generally two types of distributions; those backed by corporations who also have a Linux-for-server version that makes a lot of money, and those backed by a community of people who each work on one part of the system. The latter type is just trying to make the best operating system they can, for themselves.

And because so few people are trying to make money from the Linux Desktop, there are parts of it that are...clunky, or just outright broken. Don't get me wrong—it's truly amazing how well the Linux Desktop works considering so many of the people holding it up are volunteers who make no money out of their work. But precisely because there's not much money in it, some stuff never gets fixed because it's not interesting, or it doesn't annoy the right person.

On the flip side, you can fix *anything* yourself. Everything is open source, which means if you know how to code—or you're able to hire a programmer—you just need to change the source code.

Corporations using Linux—like Red Hat and Canonical—sometimes invest in the desktop space to fix certain problems either out of social responsibility, or because those problems also affect the server editions of Linux.

There are also companies out there that sell Linux computers, like System76, Kubuntu Focus, and Tuxedo Computers. They sell computers with Linux pre-installed. Most don't have physical store locations; only a site to order from, but they make enough money to invest some money in the desktop space. System76 in particular has made significant contributions to improving the desktop for everybody.

Linux distributions can have all sorts of priorities, but the primary one is usually making a good operating system, because the people making it are also the people using it. Depending on what you want to do, you could have a great experience or an awful one, but you can be assured everyone is doing the best they can. And hey, if you feel so inclined, you can always help out, too! You can contribute in all sorts of ways; you could contribute code, write or translate documentation, or donate to the people who build the software you use.

Desktop Linux is a community effort, not a product.

Naturally, you can use Linux without being part of the community at all. Most people do. But it's important to understand how dramatically different the structure of desktop Linux is to Windows and macOS, and that comes in large part due to its communal nature. If you understand that, many things will make much more sense, and you'll more quickly grasp how to interact with the community.

Linux and the Free Software Philosophy

Linux is Free Software. That doesn't mean it's free-of-charge (though most desktop Linux distributions do not cost anything), but instead that you are free to do whatever you want with the software. For example, you could modify the kernel code to support some hardware you want to use with Linux. This is only possible because the source code for the kernel is available freely for you to modify.

This is a consequence of the **software license** Linux is released under. Linux is distributed to users under the terms of the General Public License (Version 2). The license states that anyone may use the software for any purpose, and that the source code, which is essentially the blueprint for the software, must be given to anyone who asks for it.

You could take your modified kernel and sell it to someone else who wants to use that hardware on Linux under the terms of the license, as you can use it for any purpose, including commercial purposes. However, anyone you sell it to has the right to request the source code for the changes you made to the kernel to get the hardware to work. You are legally required to provide the source code to them, and they are then able to share the modified kernel freely or even sell it themselves.

It's a license that doesn't restrict commerce, but because it requires the code to be available and doesn't restrict others from sharing it, everyone who uses and works on the software benefits from everyone else's work.

You'll hear the term "open source" a lot, which means almost the same thing as "free software". The perspectives are simply different; "free software" is about social good, while "open source" is about being an effective model for developing good software. They end up at the same place.

The difference is subtle. If you care about "free software", you care about software being free for the sake of your freedom; if you care about "open source", you care about making the best software, which is achieved by using the open source model. If an open source application is not the best software available (and in several cases on the desktop, it simply isn't), you might feel compelled to use something "better" even if it is proprietary or non-free rather than making do with the open source application or trying to improve it.

There is nothing inherently wrong with using non-free software, but someone who cares about free software values their freedom at all costs, and would, in most cases, use a free software application even if a better non-free application was available for use. That was the entire principle on which the Linux and GNU desktop was built; that freedom is a feature which is unavailable on macOS and Windows desktops.

Many programs that you can use on Linux are also released under Free Software licenses. It's a license that allows a bunch of strangers to come together to build something with the features each developer is interested in. It's so much more powerful than just giving your software away for free but not letting anyone change it.

Everyone benefits from free software; not just software engineers. When someone adds a new feature, or fixes a bug, or removes something nefarious, you get a better version of the software as a result of someone else's work.

Linux is built on collaboration. Whether that be the largest collaboration between multinational corporations in history, or between the world's computer hobbyists. You can look at any of the code for Linux and change it if you don't like it, or to fix a mistake someone made, or to improve it. Then you can send the author the change, and they might thank you for it and include your change in the next release, which will have your name in the CONTRIBUTORS.md file. It's something anyone can get involved in, whether they're a 12-year-old[5] or a sprawling corporate entity.

That collaboration is thanks to the Free Software philosophy, which ensures nobody can profit from Linux without sharing the changes they made back to everyone else, so that everyone benefits. Isn't that kind of wonderful? And it's not like you can't make money out of it. Red Hat, the biggest Linux company, was bought by IBM in 2019 for $34 billion US dollars. That's the server space, of course, but the same philosophy applies to the desktop space.

Why use Linux on your desktop?

In my experience, there are two reasons to try Linux: curiosity and spite. If you're dissatisfied with your current operating system, why not try Linux? It's free, and you might learn something new. You might start living your life with a whole new philosophy.

---

1. My blog at jamesnorth.net chronicles some parts of my experience with Linux on the desktop over the past few years.
2. The Linux landscape changes quickly, and so information and advice may quickly become out of date. Things were very different 4 years ago, let alone 10 years ago. The desktop is more stable nowadays, but I suspect a number of things will change in the near-future.
3. The Steam Hardware Survey: https://store.steampowered.com/hwsurvey
4. https://hannahmontana.sourceforge.net/
5. *12-Year-Old Developer Brings Ubuntu's Unity Desktop Back to Life* (Rudra Saraswat): https://linuxiac.com/unity-7-6-desktop-environment-released/

Chapter 02: Glossary

What follows is a glossary of terms you may wish to read to quickly grasp the world we're entering. The glossary is written in narrative order instead of alphabetical; you should read it from top to bottom if you do decide to read it, as the terms build on each other.

Free Software

Refers to software released under a license which meets the Free Software Definition[1]. Software is considered Free Software if it provides users the four essential freedoms. The first freedom is to allow anyone to run the software for any reason. The second freedom is to be able to study and modify the program, which requires the source code. The third freedom is to be able to redistribute the software to anyone, and the fourth freedom is the ability to distribute your modified copies. Does not require software to be free-of-charge; if the software is not permitted to be sold, it does not qualify as free software.

Open Source

Refers to software released under a license that meets the Open Source Definition[2]. For software to be classified as open source, the source code must be available to any users of the software, users must be allowed to modify the source code, users must be allowed to redistribute the program, modified or unmodified, and users must be allowed to use the software for anything, including commercially. For example, users must be allowed to sell the software. Very similar to Free Software; can almost be considered a synonym, except that the goals behind the term differ from the Free Software Movement.

Free Software Movement

Refers to a group of activists with the goal of furthering the freedoms of computer users by promoting Free Software and the ideals behind it.

Libre

Another term for free software.

自由ソフトウェア

"Free Software" in Japanese. Slightly less confusing than "free software" in English.

FOSS

Stands for Free and Open Source Software. Can be used interchangeably to mean open source software that is free of charge, or a term that tries to cater to people who like the term Open Source and people who like the term Free Software.

FLOSS

Same as FOSS, but includes "Libre".

Linux

The name of a free software operating system kernel started in 1991 that is also used to refer to the operating system as a whole.

Linux Distribution

An operating system that contains the Linux kernel.

Distro

Short for Linux Distribution. Sounds hip.

Kernel

The lowest level of an operating system, responsible for managing devices and other critical duties.

GNU Project

A project to build a free software operating system that started in 1983. Often used with Linux.

Free Software Foundation

A 501(c)3 non-profit organisation founded to further the free software movement. Stewards the GNU Project.

Richard Stallman

Founder of the GNU Project and Free Software Foundation.

Linus Torvalds

Started developing the Linux kernel in 1991. Still responsible for maintaining it 33 years later.

GNU/Linux

A term the Free Software Foundation wants you to use to refer to Linux distributions to remind people of the Free Software philosophy.

Tux

A cute penguin. Mascot for the Linux kernel and operating system.

Desktop Environment

A project to build a graphical user interface that includes all the programs you need for day-to-day operation of a computer. GNOME and KDE are the most popular ones available for Linux. Windows and macOS do not have "desktop environments"; the graphical user interface is part of those operating systems.

Display Manager

Despite what the name may imply, it is a login screen that takes you to the desktop environment. Most desktop environments have their own display manager.

Window Manager

A program that renders windows and allows you to interact with them by moving, repositioning, and closing them. Desktop environments include a window manager.

Tiling Window Manager

A particular type of window manager that automatically lays out windows in a tiled layout. This is useful for productivity. However, most desktop environments do not have a tiling mode. Most tiling window managers require many hours to setup and learn to use properly, as most do not come with all the programs you need for day-to-day operations.

Package Manager

A program that handles installing, updating, removing, and searching for other programs. Usually has many features for interacting with programs.

X / X11

A "Display Server". It's a protocol from the 1980s that defines how graphics should be drawn on a computer's screen. Until the 2010s, it was the only protocol Linux used to display graphics. X11 is the 11th version of X (there has not been a new major version since 1987).

Xorg

An implementation of the X protocol. The only X implementation Linux distributions have used since the 2000s.

Wayland

A new display protocol. Designed to fix the deeply-embedded problems of the now ancient X by focusing on simplicity. More Linux distributions are starting to use Wayland by default, and in some cases, replacing X altogether.

Grok

To understand something deeply and intuitively. Applies particularly to arcane software where using it effectively is a spectacle in itself.

Upstream / Downstream

The top of the waterfall. Used to describe the chain of software distribution. The original developer of an application is “upstream” from a distribution that packages that developer’s software, and the distribution is “downstream” from the developer.

---

1. Free Software Definition: https://www.gnu.org/philosophy/free-sw.html#fs-definition
2. Open Source Definition: https://opensource.org/osd

Chapter 03: Which Linux Distribution Should You Use?

This happens to be everyone's least favourite question. It's the newbie's least favourite question because they feel overwhelmed by choice and need to rely on someone else's better judgement, and it's the Linux aficionado's least favourite question because, in an effort to provide a good answer, the aficionado needs to disregard their own sensibilities and choose something they may not personally like, but which makes a good recommendation for several reasons. Or else, the aficionado may choose to recommend their favourite distribution, which is usually not what a newbie should use.

I'm going to take a slightly different tack and ask you to choose based on what you want to do with your computer. While the answer to this question would not have made a difference even two or three years ago, the Linux world is in a transition period where it very much does matter. Most distributions offer the same software in slightly different ways, but in 2025, there are bigger gaps between distributions right now.

This transition period is due to the rise of Wayland and fall of X11. At the end of 2025, this transition is still in full swing and the dust has yet to settle.

Wayland or X11?

X11 predates the Linux kernel by almost a decade. X started being developed in 1984, but has not seen any major development since 2012. It is the system Linux distributions have been using to display graphical user interfaces (GUIs) since its inception.

However, in 2008, development started on the Wayland protocol, a new method of handling graphics for the Linux desktop. X had become monstrously large, complex and brittle, making it very difficult to add new features. In an effort not to repeat these mistakes, Wayland is significantly simpler and thinner.

Since the initial release of Wayland in 2012, Linux desktop developers have been gradually developing protocols and the subsequent implementations that enable functionality users expect and need. In 2025, there are still a few features X offers that Wayland doesn't, but the reverse is also true. Some of those features are critical to some users, but they don't matter at all to a lot of other users.

X is still barely being maintained, but it's on its way out. Some distributions are dropping support for X11-driven sessions while others are defaulting to the Wayland session but keeping the X11 session around. Most X11 bugs will not be fixed due to a lack of interest and manpower, but it is still the only option for some users.

For the longest time, Wayland was the future, and X was the present. Now, Wayland is the near-future, and X is the past, soon to be ancient history.

There is no clear answer whether you should use X11 or Wayland in 2025. It depends on your needs.

Linux Distributions to Consider

I'll provide a few recommendations based on your basic needs and dive deeper into each type of user in later chapters.

Linux Mint for most users

Linux Mint has remained largely the same throughout its existence. That's a good thing, actually—it means users know what to expect! Linux Mint won't make large, sweeping changes that users need to adapt to; it will introduce new features gradually and only when they're ready. It's a reliable system that is simple to use for any purpose. It looks fairly modern, will feel familiar to Windows users, and has a graphical user interface for pretty much everything you'd want to do.

After installation, there's a helpful guide that shows you how to setup backups and start using the system. Linux Mint has a great community and is very friendly to new users. The distribution is based on Ubuntu, so the large amount of online help available for Ubuntu will also be useful for Mint users.

Linux Mint offers three desktop environments:

- **Cinnamon:** The default experience developed and maintained by the Mint team. It's designed to work the best in Linux Mint and has the most features. It's the most modern choice.

- **XFCE:** A lightweight desktop that is configurable enough to create an environment that suits you. If your hardware is really slow, this environment has the smallest footprint. That being said, none of the environments on this list are very demanding.
- **MATE:** A traditional experience for those familiar with desktop Linux in the 2000s. There's a focus on maintaining the same experience for as long as possible, so if you want something you'll never need to learn how to re-adapt to, MATE is worth a shot.

If you don't know what to pick, pick Cinnamon. Other environments may lack features you depend on, so Cinnamon is the safest bet.

I recommend every new user go with Linux Mint, regardless of what you use your computer for. However, there is a subset of users that won't find Mint to be a great experience. If you have more than one monitor, I highly recommend Universal Blue instead.

In Linux Mint, all the environments are constrained by X11, which has trouble dealing with multiple monitors. If you have two monitors with two different resolutions and/or two different refresh rates, you will not be able to configure them separately in Mint. You'll only be able to set both monitors to the same refresh rate, which is locked to the slowest monitor.

You will also not be able to scale your monitors differently; both will need to be set to either 100% or 200% display scaling. So on at least one monitor, the text will be too small or too big. You might be able to achieve a happy medium by adjusting the font size of your interface elements, but this won't adjust the size of your window buttons (close, minimise, and maximise).

Variable Refresh Rate is also not available on X11.

That being said… if you are familiar with the command-line or willing to get your hands dirty, the xrandr utility makes it possible to set different scaling for different monitors. It involves writing an X.org configuration file for your monitors. This comes with some downsides in terms of performance and might be buggy, however.

For most people with multiple monitors, I recommend you just use Universal Blue. You can set your monitors up independently and you have granular control over scaling. And it's really easy to do, because it's available right in the graphical Settings program.

If you just have a single monitor or a laptop you don't intend to plug into an external monitor, Linux Mint is a great choice!

Find out more at https://linuxmint.com

Universal Blue for 96% of users

Universal Blue is a project that produces several operating system images based on the Fedora Atomic Desktops project.

Unless you're in the know, that probably sounds like a bunch of nonsense. The upshot of all this is that Universal Blue operating systems are based on the latest tech. They're designed to get the hell out of your way and let you use your computer.

They offer two desktop-based operating systems, both using Wayland by default:

- **Aurora:** A more Windows-like experience with plenty of configuration options to make the system your own. Simple by default; powerful when needed. Uses the KDE desktop environment.
- **Bluefin:** A more macOS-like experience that is reliable and designed to be easy to use. Offers a streamlined workflow for more advanced users. Uses the GNOME desktop environment, which is the default on most distributions.

You install all your software from the Software application on Bluefin, and the Discover application on Aurora. After you perform a system update using the System Update utility, the previous snapshot will be kept around. So if there's a bad update, you only need to select the previous snapshot when booting your system to get right back to work until the problem is fixed.

Like Mint, these distributions will suit most people. In fact, the FAQ page for Bluefin makes it clear they're targeting "96% of users" rather than everyone.

If you're a developer, you can pick the Developer Edition, which offers Docker, VS Code and Devpod out of the box.

If you want to install terminal programs (like Neovim), the best way to do that is through Homebrew, though you can also use distrobox if you prefer.

Universal Blue's operating systems are "immutable", which means the base system is generally untouched. The applications you install through the Software program go on top of the base system without interfering with it. There is a clear line drawn between "the system" and "the user's software". This is mostly an interesting technical detail; the upshot of this is that it reduces system breakage by not allowing the system and the user's software to interact directly with each other.

They're a great place to start with Linux in 2025 if you're looking for the latest and greatest.

Find out more at https://universal-blue.org

- Download Bluefin at https://projectbluefin.io
- Download Aurora at https://getaurora.dev

Debian for Professional Artists

This is a rather strange category, but its inclusion is necessary as artists are one of the largest casualties of this rough transition period between X11 and Wayland.

If you only need to use a graphics tablet on occasion or are a casual artist who doesn't care about colour accuracy, go for Universal Blue.

If you're a professional artist, Debian is the best choice at the end of 2024, and it's unlikely things will be much different by the end of 2025.

I recommend installing Debian with KDE, which has the best graphics tablet settings. You'll be able to calibrate your monitor for colour accuracy and configure your graphics tablet just the way you like it.

You can calibrate your monitor in Linux Mint, too, but I recommend Debian with KDE because Cinnamon's graphics tablet settings are not as advanced. With xsetwacom, you can set things up just the same regardless of whether you're on Linux Mint with Cinnamon or Debian with KDE; as long as you're using X11, it will work. That being said, you don't need the command line if you're working with KDE, so it's a friendlier experience.

Debian focuses on creating a reliable experience by freezing the software it offers in time and only offering security fixes. Then, a few years later when the next version of Debian is released, all software is upgraded to the latest stable version and frozen for the next few years.

For this reason, Debian will be one of the last distributions to drop X11 as it intentionally lags so far behind other distributions. This is perfect for an artist's production machine; you can be sure your software will not change for at least a few years, and by then, hopefully all the kinks in Wayland will be worked out.

Got an Apple Silicon Mac? Try Asahi Linux!

If you own a Mac produced after 2020 with an Apple Silicon chip, your only real option right now is Asahi Linux, offered through Fedora Asahi Remix. But don't worry; it's a good option. The Asahi Linux project has put considerable effort into reverse-engineering Apple's hardware to provide top-tier support for it on Linux. They've done such a good job, in fact, that they've developed drivers which support the highest standards of OpenGL and Vulkan, which means they offer a better gaming experience than macOS.

You can play more video games with a better experience on your Mac hardware with Asahi Linux.

The downside is they don't yet support all hardware features (check the Device Support page) or M3 and M4 chips, but they're working on it. It's shocking how much progress the Asahi Linux team has made in such a short period of time, and they've managed a number of impressive technical innovations along the way. It should be noted that as Asahi is a new distribution, they do not support X11 and only offer a Wayland session.

Their ultimate goal is to land their drivers in the Linux kernel, which means any Linux distribution will offer the same great support for newer Macs; not just Asahi.

You can learn more at their website: https://asahilinux.org

If you own an older Intel Mac (produced before 2020), any distribution will offer the same level of support for your device, so you can choose whichever you like.

How to Install Linux

Now that you know what distribution to pick, you need to install it. The process is usually the same, regardless of distribution. The distribution will have instructions on installing the operating system, but the following is a general guide.

Before you do *anything*, back up the data on your computer, as you may overwrite it in the installation process. You can setup a "dual-boot", which keeps both operating systems on the same drive, but this is prone to breakage. If you want to do this, I recommend getting a second drive just for Linux.

First, download the ISO file for the distribution. Next, grab a USB flash drive, which is what you'll "flash" the ISO file to.

To flash the distribution onto the USB drive, you need to install a program like Balena Etcher, which can be downloaded from etcher.balena.io.

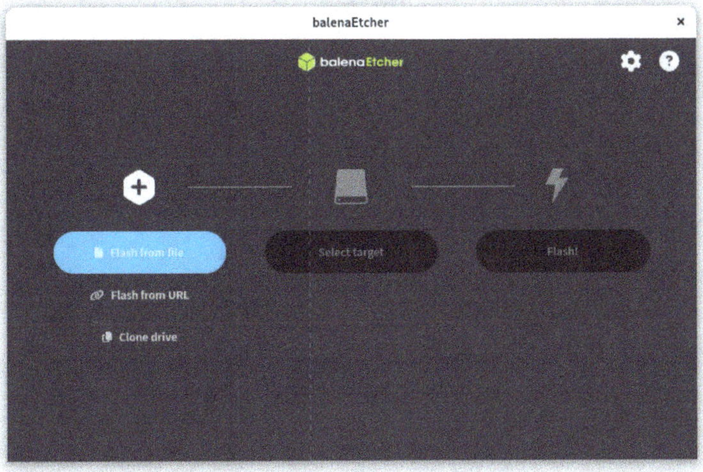

Insert the USB drive into your computer and launch Balena Etcher. Then find the ISO file, select your drive, and click Flash.

Now, you need to boot from the USB drive. To do that, you first need to reboot your computer. While it boots up, you need to press a particular key to get the boot menu to appear. The key will be different depending on your computer, but a few common ones are ESC, F11, and DEL. You should find the correct key in either your motherboard's manual or by searching online for your computer model.

Once you get the boot menu to appear, select your USB drive with the arrow keys and press enter to boot from it.

The installer for your distribution will launch. At this point, you only need to follow the prompts to install the distribution. If you're on Linux Mint and want to setup a dual-boot between Windows and Linux Mint on the same drive (for example, on your laptop), you need to select "Install Linux Mint alongside Windows".

Once the installation is done, you will usually be told to unplug the USB drive and the system will reboot into your newly-installed Linux distribution.

All installation processes (even Windows) follow this general procedure. The specifics of these instructions may differ depending on the distribution, so always follow your distribution's official instructions.

Chapter 04: Installing Software on Linux

So, you've got your chosen Linux distribution installed. What now?

Regardless of what you want to do with your computer, you need some software to get things done. While a few applications will be installed by default (some distributions install more than others), you'll likely need to go out and find more.

If you're a Windows user, you'll quickly find that installing software on Linux is quite different to what you're used to.

Software Installation Utilities

Instead of searching for applications on the open web, your operating system provides you with a few tools to install software from a "repository", which is a collection of software from trusted sources that you can quickly install.

Using the Graphical Software Store

The store may be called something different depending on the distribution you've chosen. Usually, it's called "Software", "Discover", or "App Store". This is the easiest and preferred method of installing software.

Open the store and search for an application you want to install. When you click on it, you should find an Install button on the page.

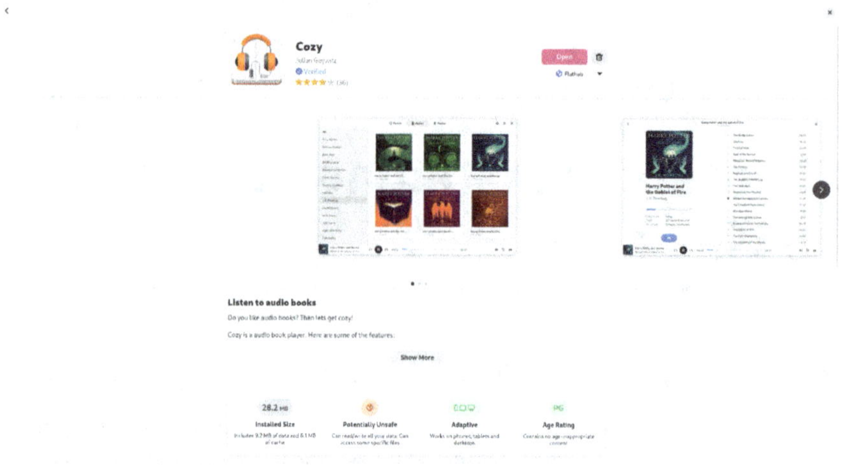

The Store aggregates several installation methods together. You can usually install Flatpaks or Distribution Packages from the Store.

The two methods are slightly different:

- **Flatpak:** Software available on Flathub, a Linux App Store which offers more than 2,600 applications at the time of writing. About 50% of these applications are maintained by the developer themselves, and are the most up-to-date version.

  These applications are sandboxed, which means you can manage their permissions; for example, you may not want an application to know what's in your home folder. These are the only types of applications you can install on Universal Blue operating systems from the Store. You can rollback to previous versions of an application if there are issues with the latest version without affecting other applications or your base system.

- **Distribution Package:** Software available directly from your distribution. These packages are not maintained by the original developer. Depending on your distribution, the package may be the latest release or years old; Debian has older packages while Linux Mint usually has newer packages.

  These applications are not sandboxed, so you cannot manage their permissions, but some applications may need privileged access to work correctly. You cannot rollback to previous versions of an application easily; the base system and other applications depend on the same shared libraries, so rolling back one application may break others.

You can run into trouble with both types of packages, so one is not necessarily better than the other. Some applications don't work at all in a sandbox, but most will be fine. In 2025, I would recommend trying the Flatpak application first, and then falling back to the distribution package if you face issues.

Package Managers

Linux distributions come with a command-line package management tool you can use to install, uninstall, and find distribution packages. For Linux Mint, you have apt, and it's apt for Debian as well. Fedora-based distributions like Asahi come with DNF, but atomic variants like Universal Blue use rpm-ostree for layering on distribution packages, though this will be replaced with DNF5 sometime in 2025.

If you use Arch, you'll be interacting with a tool called "pacman".

There are different commands for interacting with each tool. You can check the manpage (by entering "man apt" for example) or check your distribution's documentation for help. They are particularly useful for automating installation, but you may find yourself needing to rely on them to install command-line programs like Wine, ffmpeg, or Neovim, as they aren't available to install from the Store application.

Snap Packages

Snap packages are analogous to Flatpak packages. The packages are sandboxed, they work for every distribution, and you can install them from the Store application (if it supports it).

However, none of the distributions I recommended in the previous chapter support Snap by default, so you will need to set it up if you want to install Snap packages. Ubuntu is one of the only distributions that supports Snaps by default—which you would expect, as Canonical develops both of them.

I do not personally know of an application available from the Snap Store that is not available from Flathub or as a distribution package, so I don't think there is much point installing it on a distribution aside from Ubuntu.

I'll discuss Snaps in greater detail in a later chapter.

Other Installation Methods

There are yet more installation methods you can try, but these aren't "preferred" methods. These are methods to try when the above options aren't available or don't work. With any luck, the Store will have everything you want and you won't even need to think about these methods!

Appimages

Some developers distribute their software only as Appimages. For example, until 2024, Bitwarden only offered an Appimage, but they now maintain the Flatpak package on Flathub. Krita only officially offers an Appimage.

Appimages are a bundle of (ideally) everything the software needs to work on any Linux distribution. They are much like a portable EXE on Windows or a DMG on macOS. When you download the file, you need to open your file manager and give the Appimage executable permission. Then, you can run it from your file manager.

You won't be able to pin Appimages to your dock/taskbar without creating a .desktop file. Appimages are not sandboxed, so you face permission issues like you might with Flatpak, but you also can't update them easily; you need to download a new Appimage when the developer pushes an update.

Appimages work well enough, but you should prefer distribution packages or Flatpaks in most cases so you don't have too many of them to manage on your system. Or consider installing an Appimage manager like Gear Lever from Flathub.

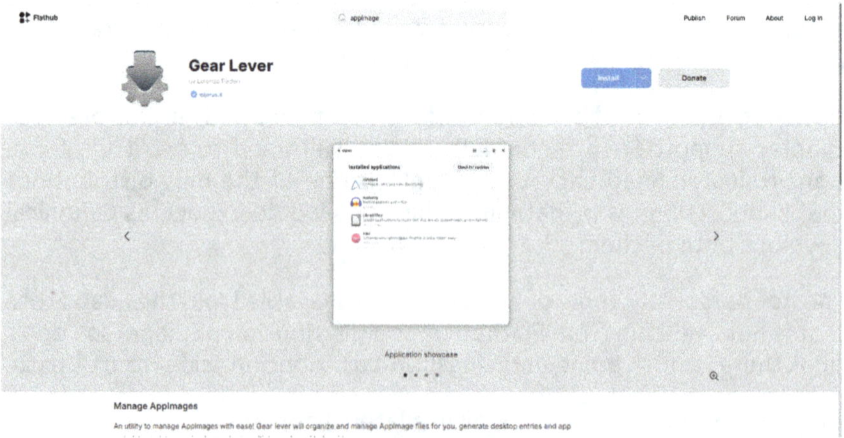

pip, npm, cargo, and Other Programming Language Package Managers

This might get a bit technical if you're not a software developer, but the takeaway is: as part of the toolset developers make use of to develop software, they generally have access to a package manager just for libraries and tools built using that programming language by other developers. For Python, that's pip; for NodeJS, that's npm; and for Rust, that's Cargo.

By installing the development tools for one of these languages through your distribution packages, you can use the package manager to install software developed in those languages. Be aware however that, depending on where these package managers install files, it might cause conflicts with your distribution package manger. pip is notorious for this, and most distributions will disable its system-wide package management; you'll need to work around this.

This is not the intended use case for these package managers; most of the time, developers use them to install libraries, not full-blown applications.

Distrobox

This is quite a new method of installation. And it's a little hacky. Distrobox is a set of shell scripts that manage Podman containers and help them integrate better with your desktop system. This sounds pretty technical, but using it is pretty easy if you're willing to use the command line.

You can install other distributions with Distrobox and install the distribution packages using that distribution's package manager. It's common for other distributions to package particular applications or particular versions another doesn't. You can use Box Buddy, a graphical tool, instead of the distrobox command-line tools to manage these containers.

It's a little hacky—especially for more complicated applications—but works pretty well for command-line applications.

Compile it From Source!

Lastly—and this is the most painful option—you can compile the application from source. This sounds scary, but really it's mostly frustrating. Even for software developers who do this thing all the time, it's a big chore that can involve a lot of trial and error.

If it's a simple program, you might just need to install a few libraries and run the build/install commands, and you're done. If not...prepare to spend the next hour or so stockpiling specific library versions and debugging errors of varying helpfulness.

You might also compile something from source when you want a newer version of some software that's only available as an outdated distribution package. A few years ago, this was your only option for getting newer software, but thanks to Flatpak, there's a much easier way.

That sure sounds like a lot of software installation methods!

You're not wrong. Though, even on macOS, you still need to deal with .pkg and .dmg files, or you could install from the App Store, or you could install from Homebrew/MacPorts, and you've got the programming language package managers too. It's a similar story on Windows.

In this case, having options isn't a bad thing. It means you have something else to try if what you want isn't available with your preferred method. You probably won't need to worry about anything other than what's available in the Store application for a long time! It is, however, good to know your options.

Chapter 05: Day in the Life of a Linux User

You're running Linux, and you know how to install software. Now, let's take a tour through the applications available on Linux so you can start your first Day as a Linux User.

Does the Software You Use Work on Linux?

The following table is a quick reference you can use to ascertain whether an application you use works on Linux. It's an index of common applications, and is not comprehensive.

Application	**Works on Linux?**	**Similar**
Autodesk Maya	✅ Yep	Blender
Nuke	✅ Yep	Natron
Houdini	✅ Yep	
DaVinci Resolve	✅ Yep	Kdenlive, Lightworks
Studio One	✅ Yep	Kdenlive, Lightworks
Unity Engine	✅ Yep	Godot
Unreal Engine	✅ Yep	Godot
Zoom	✅ Yep	
OBS Studio	✅ Yep	
Visual Studio Code	✅ Yep	
Jetbrains IDEs	✅ Yep	

Signal Desktop	✅ Yep	
Discord	✅ Yep	
Slack	✅ Yep	
Google Chrome	✅ Yep	Firefox
Microsoft Office	⚠️ Kinda, with Crossover	Office.com, LibreOffice, OnlyOffice
Microsoft Outlook (Microsoft Exchange Mailboxes)	❌ Nope	GNOME Evolution; Thunderbird (Experimental); Davmail
Clip Studio Paint	❌ Nope	Krita
Affinity Creative Suite	⚠️ Kinda, with a Custom Build of Wine	GIMP, Krita, Inkscape, Scribus
Adobe Acrobat	❌ Not anymore	Acrobat (Web), Firefox as a Reader/ Annotator, Okular (as a reader), Master PDF Editor
Adobe Photoshop	❌ Nope	Photoshop (Web), Photopea, Canva GIMP
Adobe Illustrator	❌ Nope	Illustrator (Web), Inkscape
Adobe Lightroom	❌ Nope	Lightroom (Web), darktable, RawTherapee
Adobe inDesign	❌ Nope	Scribus, Viva Designer
Adobe Premiere Pro	❌ Nope	DaVicini Resolve, Lightworks, Kdenlive
Adobe After Effects	❌ Nope	DaVinci Resolve's Fusion Tab, Friction
Adobe Audition	❌ Nope	Audacity, Ardour, Reaper, Bitwig

AutoCAD	❌ Nope	AutoCAD (Web), BricsCAD, FreeCAD, LibreCAD, Fusion 360 (Web)

The rest of the chapter will break down day-to-day computing tasks and how/whether you can accomplish them on Linux.

Web Browser

The most important application on any computer—be it mobile or desktop—is the web browser. You'll be glad to hear that on Linux, you can continue to use your favourite browser (as long as it isn't Safari). Google Chrome, Firefox, Opera, and even Microsoft Edge can all be used on Linux.

Most distributions will include Firefox by default, so I recommend giving Firefox a shot first. It works just as well as Chrome in most cases. If you really want Chrome, you can easily install it on any distribution.

On Linux Mint, you can install Google Chrome by downloading the .deb package from Google's website. On Universal Blue, the best way is by installing the unofficial Google Chrome Flatpak maintained by the community. You can install it from the Software/Discover application.

Most distributions will offer a distribution package for Chromium, which is the free software version of Google Chrome without sync and a few other features. If you don't need everything Chrome offers, Chromium is a better choice.

Web browsers work just as well on Linux as they do on Windows or macOS, so if your browser is the main thing you use, not much will change for you. There are two things to watch out for, though.

Caveat 1: Using Streaming Services on Linux

Whether it's Netflix, Binge, Prime Video, Crunchyroll, HiDive, or any of the other many streaming services available today, you can use most of them on Linux with the exception of Peacock.[1] This does come with a limitation in most cases, however.

Almost all paid streaming services encumber their content with DRM. DRM stands for "Digital Rights Management"; it is a technological measure for restricting what you can do with the content these services serve you. It tries to prevent users from copying or recording the show or movie you're watching and sharing it with others.

On Microsoft Windows, if you try to record Netflix with a screen recording application, the operating system will render the entire site black and stop playing the video so you cannot record anything. There is a high level of integration between the streaming service's DRM and the operating system, so the streaming service has a high level of trust that the operating system can prevent you from copying their shows. The same is true of macOS and Google's Chromebooks.

This DRM will work on Linux browsers like Firefox and Chrome too, but Linux won't attempt to stop you from recording the streaming service's shows. For this reason, Netflix limits the maximum video resolution to 720p (Standard HD) on Linux.[2] Netflix will serve content up to 2160p on other operating systems it trusts more.

This is a bitter pill to swallow, especially when you're paying for the privilege of watching these shows. It's a shame these streaming services don't trust their customers enough not to restrict their video quality, but this is still a big improvement on the previous state of affairs.

Until 2014, streaming services like Netflix didn't work on Linux at all. That year, the WorldWide Web Consortium (W3C) established the DRM Encrypted Media Extensions (EME), which was a standardised way of offering DRM directly in the browser as opposed to using third-party frameworks like Silverlight. This move was controversial[3], but it's why Linux users can use streaming services at all today.

Caveat 2: Websites that Block Linux User Agents

There are a few websites out there that have made the decision to block Linux browsers based on the User Agent String. This is a very weak block that can be easily circumvented by using a User Agent Switcher extension. There are a number of them available on both the Mozilla and Chrome extension stores. You can use these switchers to tell the website your browser is actually running on a Windows computer, and the website will believe it.

It's unlikely you'll run into many websites doing this, but if you do, you now know how to get around it.

Email

If you use webmail like Gmail to read and send emails, you can just use your web browser for your email. If, however, you use an email client like Outlook, you'll want to use an email client on Linux, too.

There are several clients to choose from on Linux. The most popular option is Thunderbird, which is available on Windows, macOS, Linux, and Android. Thunderbird was originally a Mozilla project that was adopted by the community and has become one of the most well-funded free software applications available for desktop Linux. It has a lot of features, and it's around for the long haul. Millions of people love the Thunderbird email client, and it's what I use.

If you want a client that fits in well with your desktop environment, there's also Geary for GNOME or KMail for KDE.

If You Have a Microsoft Exchange Email Account...

Microsoft Exchange is one of the few reasons anyone runs a Windows server anymore. If there was one thing Microsoft got right, it was email. It's no surprise, then, that Microsoft Exchange is popular in certain circles—particularly among business people. However, Exchange makes use of proprietary protocols instead of the standard email protocols everyone else uses, so you have a more limited selection of clients to choose from.

GNOME Evolution is the only free software, free-of-charge client that really has great support for Microsoft Exchange. Novell backed the development of this email client in the 2000s after their purchase of Ximian, and while the company is no longer interested in the client, it still works great with Microsoft Exchange and is maintained by a few developers.

The client looks a little dated and is highly unlikely to ever be updated to a modern version of GTK, but it has a huge number of features and it's easy to get productive with.

If you don't like Evolution, Thunderbird started adding support for Microsoft Exchange protocols in 2024. It currently only supports fetching and sending mail through the Exchange Web Services (EWS) protocol with no support for calendaring.

Otherwise, you might look into a project called Davmail: https://davmail.sourceforge.net

Davmail is a gateway that sits in front of whichever email client you want to use and translates back and forth from standard email protocols to Exchange's proprietary protocols. Instead of connecting to your Exchange server in your emai client, you connect to Davmail's local server running on your machine.

I've used several of these solutions when I needed to connect to an Exchange server for a few years. Evolution worked the best, but Davmail let me use Thunderbird, which is my preferred client. Thunderbird's Exchange support is still experimental, so it's not something to rely on just yet.

Nowadays, I run Smartermail[4] instead of Microsoft Exchange on the server, which does support standard email protocols. If you have decision-making abilities in your business, Smartermail is something to look into. There are rumours that Microsoft is looking to drop their standalone Exchange product and only offer Exchange with their own cloud in the future.

Office Suite

I'll give it to you straight: Microsoft does not offer their Office products on Linux. That means no Word, Powerpoint, Excel, or Outlook.

But before you panic, you've still got a few options.

Microsoft Office in Your Web Browser

Microsoft provides more limited, lightweight versions of the Microsoft Office Suite on the web at Office.com. These will work on any modern browser, so they work great on Linux.

Give it a try; they might fit your needs. If not, try one of the alternatives below.

Google Workspace / G Suite / Google Docs

Google Workspace is the most popular alternative to Microsoft Office, and for good reason. It's very easy to collaborate with someone else, and all the Google webapps have plenty of advanced features. At least on the web, no other office suite comes close.

Google Docs, Google Sheets, and Google Slides are the respective alternatives to Word, Excel, and Powerpoint. They work great on Linux in Google Chrome.

All of them are free to use, though there's an optional subscription if you want more features.

LibreOffice Suite

LibreOffice is a free software, free-of-charge productivity suite. The LibreOffice Suite includes a word processor called Writer, a presentation program called Impress, and a spreadsheeting program called Calc. If you want an Outlook alternative, you can try one of the clients mentioned in the previous section.

LibreOffice is compatible with Microsoft Office file formats like .docx, and Microsoft Word can actually read LibreOffice's file formats like .odt, so there's an opportunity for interchange between the two suites. It's not perfect, but it will get the job done in most cases.

If you're a home user, LibreOffice will most likely suit you fine. You might even be using OpenOffice already, which is the predecessor to LibreOffice.

OpenOffice has not been actively developed for many years and does not receive security updates to patch known vulnerabilities. LibreOffice is an actively-developed version of OpenOffice, so if you're still using OpenOffice, you should move onto LibreOffice.

Running Microsoft Office Through CrossOver

If you find you really need the Microsoft Office desktop programs and can accept no substitutes, look into CrossOver. Codeweavers have been offering their compatibility software, CrossOver, for running Windows programs like Microsoft Office on Linux since the 1990s. You can trial CrossOver for 14 days to see if it works for you, and if it does, you can make a one-time purchase with optional yearly upgrades.

I used Microsoft Word through CrossOver for several months with a few crashes, but was otherwise able to use it fine. I had less luck with Powerpoint, but CrossOver improves with every release. You'll need to do your own testing to be sure.

Running Microsoft Office in a Windows Virtual Machine

As a last resort, you can create a Windows virtual machine using the GNOME Boxes application and run your Microsoft Office programs within the virtual machine. As they aren't graphically intensive applications, they will run fine on a computer with enough resources. You won't have compatibility problems, but you might struggle to figure out how best to transfer files between the virtual machine and your host machine.

Ebooks and Audiobooks

I assume from the fact you're reading this book that you think favourably of books in general. You'll be able to continue doing plenty of reading on your Linux machine.

Ebook Readers

If you enjoy reading ebooks on your computer as I do, you've got a great selection of ebook readers to choose from on Linux.

My favourite EPUB reader is Foliate, which you can install from Flathub. It looks beautiful and there are many ways to adjust the layout. If you want something with even more configuration options, try Calibre, which most distributions have a distribution package for.

Both KDE and GNOME have good PDF readers. KDE has Okular and GNOME has Papers. I use Okular even on Windows because it's so much better than anything else available. But if you don't like either, you can use Firefox or Chromium's built-in PDF readers, too.

Cozy for Audiobooks

If you listen to a lot of Audiobooks, Cozy is a great way of managing and listening to your library. It's simple, beautiful, and works offline.

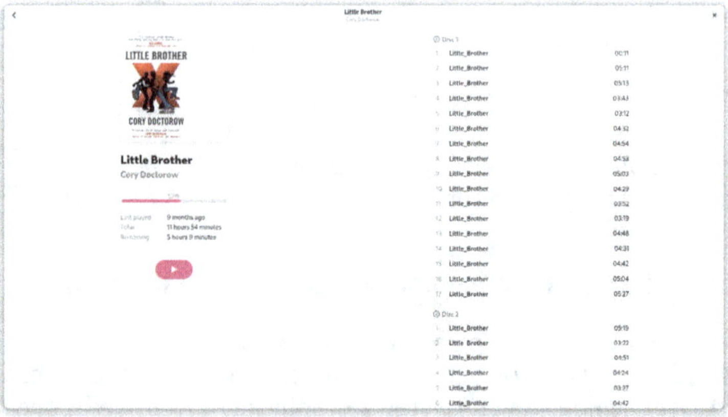

You can install Cozy from Flathub.

Why You Should Buy DRM-Free Books

While Linux has great applications for reading ebooks and audiobooks, they will only work with DRM-free books. If you buy your books from Amazon, most of them will be encumbered by DRM, and you'll need to use the Kindle Cloud Reader to read them. For this reason, I don't recommend buying your ebooks and audiobooks from Amazon.

When you buy from Amazon, you're playing with Fire. You don't own any of the digital products you buy. There's a chance Amazon will ban your account and confiscate all your books if they suspect you of doing something they don't like. This is something I've taken to calling the Amazon Swindle.[5]

Where to Buy DRM-Free Books

You can get DRM-free ebooks that you actually do own from Smashwords and Leanpub. Some authors and publishers will sell DRM-free books directly, like Tor Books, or Cory Doctorow. You can sometimes get DRM-free ebooks from Kobo—they'll say "(DRM-FREE)" under "eBook Details" at the bottom of the page.

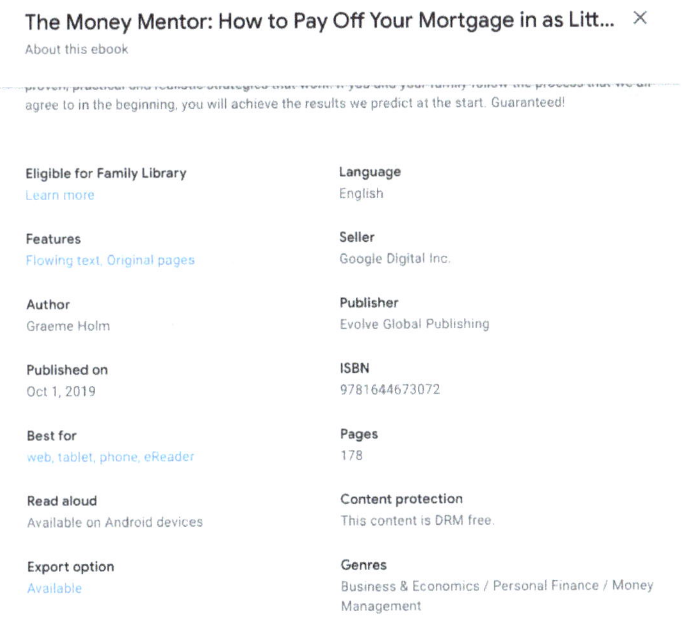

Google Play sometimes offers DRM-free downloads for ebooks. You can tell whether a book is encumbered by DRM by clicking "About this ebook" and scrolling down to "Content protection"; if it is, it will say, "This content is DRM free."

If you enjoy public domain books, Standard Ebooks has a big selection of very high-quality DRM-free ebook files available for download. If you don't know what to read, I recommend starting with one of the early Agatha Christie novels.

If you enjoy audiobooks, check out Libro.fm, which offers over 500,000 DRM-free audiobooks for sale. Google Play sells DRM-free audiobooks too.

If you enjoy public domain books, check out Librivox. Narrators (both amateur and professional) have lent their voice to public domain books and released their narration to the public domain. All downloads are DRM-free.

Video Players

If you're not watching videos in your browser, you need a video player. VLC has been the golden standard for a long time, and it's available on Linux too. If you've never used VLC before, just know that you can play almost anything with it, and it has an insane number of features. You can even do stuff like convert video to audio inside it.

If anything...it's actually too big. I prefer a player that is smaller and lighter with a nicer interface.

If you feel the same way, you might like Celluloid, the mpv-based video player that uses GTK for its interface. It's compatible with all mpv plugins and configuration files, but the interface makes it easier to use out of the box.

What's mpv, you ask? It's a media player that plays just as many formats as VLC, but it can be used in the command-line without a graphical interface. It's often used as a library to power other media players like Celluloid.

I use plain mpv with a selection of scripts and configuration options designed to make it work just how I want, but there's a learning curve for it. So, you would be better off starting with a mpv frontend like Celluloid where all the features are available in the interface rather than hidden behind a keybind.

DVDs and Blu-rays

DVDs and Blu-Rays are encumbered by DRM. If you've been keeping up so far, that means yet another conglomeration of companies has conspired to make it as hard as possible for you to use your legally-acquired discs.

I don't think you can make a serious attempt at using desktop Linux without accidentally becoming an advocate for the total extinction of DRM.

At least in the case of DVDs, a library called "libdvdcss" is included with VLC that allows you to play any DVD from any region on your Linux computer. The use of this library is controversial in some countries, though it has never been legally challenged. Because VLC comes included with this library, you might wish to avoid VLC if you are unsure whether the use of the library is legal in your country.

For Blu-Rays, there are no legal options to play them on Linux. I would recommend not buying Blu-Rays if you intend to play them on your Linux computer, as no one sells a software Blu-Ray player for Linux that allows you to legally play them.

Steam & Games

Linux is great for gaming! This wasn't true before the 2020s, but it's hard to say otherwise since the rise of Proton and the great success of the Steam Deck.

Steam is available natively for Linux and Valve have created their own Linux operating system. Their support for Linux is easily the best in the gaming industry.

There are almost as many native Linux games on Steam as there are for macOS, and considerably less macOS games than are available for Windows (99.99% of them). However, most of those Windows games can also be played on Linux thanks to Proton.

Proton is a compatibility layer created by Valve Software in collaboration with Codeweavers that makes Windows games work on Linux. It is very successful at this, though not every game is playable on Linux yet.

It's very easy to enable Proton:

Just install Steam, launch it, click Steam in the top left corner and click Settings.

Then click Compatibility and click Enable Steam Play for supported titles and click Enable Steam Play for all other titles.

Now you can try to play any game in your Steam Library. Many will work fine. If you're having trouble, check protondb.com, an unofficial compatibility database for Proton, for tweaks other users have tried.

What about the Epic Store?

Heroic Games Launcher makes it easy to try playing games from the Epic Store on Linux. But because Epic doesn't support Linux like Valve does, the game may not play as well or at all, and there's nowhere to submit an issue about it.

What about GOG and itch.io?

If the game you want to play has a native Linux version, it will probably work. If it only has a Windows version, you can probably also get it to work, but you'll need to figure out how to yourself.

Multiplayer Games

While most singleplayer games work great through Proton, more than half of the games that require anti-cheat software to be installed on the user's computer block Linux users from playing. There's nothing to be done about this, as developers consider Linux users more trouble than they're worth because it's too hard to detect cheating on Linux.

All of the Valve multiplayer games like CounterStrike, Team Fortress, and DOTA 2 work on Linux because they rely on server-side anti-cheat instead of client-side anti-cheat software. There are a number of other multiplayer games with anti-cheat that work on Linux too, but your favourite game may not.

Playing Japanese Visual Novels on Linux

I happen to be a big fan of visual novels. I like playing the original Japanese versions. The thing is, most Japanese publishers do not distribute their games to the Steam store; they use Japanese stores like DMM and DLsite. This is a problem because Steam customers aren't buying these games, so Valve has no reason to work specifically on getting them to work on Linux.

As a result, while visual novels sold on these Japanese stores do often work through Wine, the DRM usually doesn't. These games use DRM that no Steam games use, and they're rather niche. It's possible that Wine developers may happen into adding support for the features these DRM mechanisms rely on, but they tend to rely on obscure functionality.

That being said, there are a lot of Japanese visual novels that are released without DRM. I recommend buying those games.

Where possible, you should buy "dual-language" visual novels, which are available in both English and Japanese. These are sold by localisation companies that have retained the original Japanese script in the English release. These are the best versions to buy, because localisation companies usually transplant the visual novel into an engine that has better compatibility, and because this engine is usually Ren'Py, they sometimes release native Linux versions, too.

Otherwise, if you're buying from Japanese vendors, you should try DLsite. They have a clear warning on the store page when the game contains DRM, and no warning when it doesn't. They are the only Japanese vendor I know of that sells games without DRM.

If you have the money, you should buy physical versions of visual novels, as they are less likely to contain DRM. However, before making the purchase, you should visit the VNDB page, which classifies whether a particular release of that visual novel contains DRM.

The full DRM statistics for VNDB are available here: https://vndb.org/r/drm.

If you want more information about running Japanese visual novels on Linux, please visit wiki.vncompat.org

This Wiki could itself be made into a book if I had the inclination. I spent months writing and editing the content with a friend. It contains everything there is to know about the subject, from buying the games to advanced troubleshooting, down to how Wine really works.

It's also the only extensive visual novel guide on the internet I am aware of that contains no information on acquiring illegally-redistributed game files for visual novels and only promotes legal options.

Screen Recording & Screenshots

GNOME comes included with both a screenshot and screen recording tool that you can use by pressing the Printscreen button on your computer. This should suffice for simple situations.

If you have more complex needs, consider OBS Studio. It's more advanced, but that also means it's more complicated. It is a professional recording tool used for both offline recording and livestreaming by a lot of people, and you've probably heard of it before. It works great on Linux—you should try the Flatpak version first.

Creative Software

Creative software does exist on Linux, but if you're a professional, the programs you use for work are probably not available.

Here's an overview of the landscape:

Audio Production & Editing

- **Audacity:** If you're in the audio industry at all, you've likely already heard of and even used Audacity. It's a free software application for recording and editing audio that has recently gotten a lot of development. It's a general audio editing tool that should cover any of your needs.
- **Ardour, Bitwig, and Reaper:** These applications are full-fledged Digital Audio Workstations. Ardour is a paid free software application, and the other two are paid proprietary applications. These applications are best for recording, mixing, and working with music. Audacity will likely be easier to use if you just need to edit some audio, but you might need the professional features in these applications instead.

3D & VFX

If you have a job in VFX or 3D, a lot of professional applications are actually available on Linux. You've got access to Blender, Maya, Nuke, and Houdini.

There are other professional 3D applications not available on Linux, but you can certainly get a lot done with what is available.

Art

Professional artists like David Revoy have created some amazing art with Krita, the free software art program that came out of KDE. Not being much of an artist myself, I can't give you a professional opinion on how it compares to software like Clip Studio Paint, but enough artists swear by it that I'm not shy about recommending it to artists wanting to try out Linux.

If you work with vector graphics, Inkscape is the way to go. There's also the Adobe Illustrator web version at illustrator.adobe.com.

Video Editing

There are a huge number of choices for non-linear video editors (NLEs) regardless of the operating system. I'll keep it to just three:

- **DaVinci Resolve**: A free NLE with an insane number of features. People in Hollywood use this thing to work on movies—though they mainly use it for the colour grading tools, as in the industry, video production is split between different purpose-built tools. DaVinci Resolve's colour grading tools are the best in the world, but it's a great general-purpose NLE now, too. On Linux, it has no support for H.264 video and AAC audio, but otherwise has the same featureset as its Windows and macOS versions.
- **Kdenlive:** An open-source, free NLE that came out of KDE and has been around for a long time. It's not as reliable or professional as DaVinci Resolve, but you can do a lot with it. At the end of 2024, Kdenlive got a UI redesign that makes its effects workflow more efficient. Its developers are serious about adding professional features to Kdenlive and making it more powerful and reliable.
- **Lightworks:** A paid, proprietary NLE that has been around since the 1990s. It has been used to cut many great films—famously Pulp Fiction in 1993, and more recently Killers Of The Flower Moon. It can handle many video and audio codecs on Linux, including H.264 and AAC. Its editing tools are unparalleled, and its colour grading tools are better than Kdenlive. It's a reliable, professional NLE that comes with no limitations on Linux, so it's a nice middle ground between Kdenlive and Resolve.

Image Manipulation & RAW Processing

For image manipulation, the GNU Image Manipulation Program (GIMP) has always been the chief recommendation on Linux. The GIMP 2.x series has several big limitations compared to its peers like Photoshop, but the long-anticipated GIMP 3 is due out sometime in 2025 with the addition of some highly necessary features that brings it up to speed. The second release candidate was released at the end of December 2024.

You could also use Photoshop on the web at photoshop.adobe.com or Photopea, which I've found works better than Adobe's web version, at photopea.com.

If you're into photography, you definitely want an application for processing your RAWs. Darktable and RawTherapee are the go-to applications for this on Linux. In a pinch, you can also use Adobe Lightroom on the web at lightroom.adobe.com

Rolling Back to a Previous Version of an Application

If you've just updated an application and the new version isn't working out for you for some reason (some functionality is broken, or the entire thing is broken), you need to rollback to the previous version.

Depending on the type of package, there are a few ways to do that. If it was a distribution package, you're pretty much out of luck. You could try rolling back using your package manager (this requires using terminal commands), but this isn't recommended.

You might need to rollback a library that one of your system components depends on, which might break that component, leaving you with a hosed system. Or, if you rollback the system component too, you might be leaving yourself open to a vulnerability.

In these situations, I usually uninstall the distribution package and install the application as either a Flatpak or Appimage.

After that, you need to install the Warehouse application, which is itself a Flatpak application. This application will allow you to easily rollback other applications. Just click on the application, click Version, and click Change Version. You'll be presented with a list of previous versions to downgrade to; it's as simple as that.

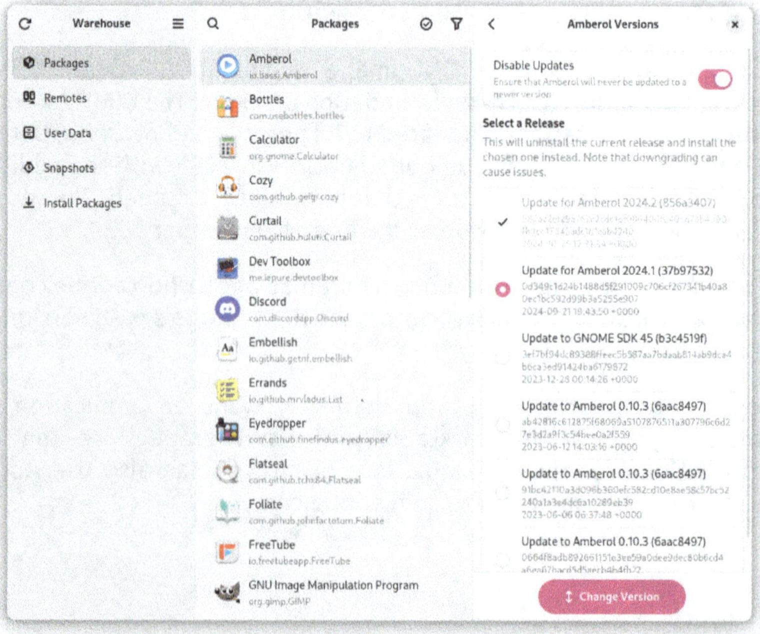

There's a lot of other handy stuff you can do in Warehouse, too, so I recommend exploring it.

With Appimages, all you need to do is run your older Appimage executable instead of the new one.

Logs

I highly recommend installing the Logs application, which is available on Flathub. If you ever face a weird issue or a crash, check the Logs application. It arranges system logs in a nice, readable interface that makes it easy to copy output from.

Terminal Emulator

Linux users famously can't do without their Terminal Emulators—which is a fancy word for an application that lets you enter commands into your computer. Every desktop environment comes with its own terminal emulator, and those are usually fine in most circumstances.

That being said, if you find yourself using the terminal a lot, you might want something more comfortable or powerful. I recommend Ptyxis if you want something with a lot of features, or Alacritty if you want something simple and fast. If you use Zellij, you should definitely use Alacritty, as the only terminal emulator I know the copy-to-clipboard feature works on is Alacritty.

---

1. Peacock is the only streaming service I know of that blocks Linux, and even blocks Chromebooks in some cases. I cannot use the service because it is only available in the United States, so I can only rely on what other users say.
2. Netflix lists Linux browser requirements and max video resolution on their help page: https://help.netflix.com/en/node/30081
3. The EFF has a great article covering the development of EME and what it means for the web: https://www.eff.org/deeplinks/2017/10/drms-dead-canary-how-we-just-lost-web-what-we-learned-it-and-what-we-need-do-next
4. Smartermail is a paid, proprietary alternative to Microsoft Exchange you can run on a Windows or Linux server: https://www.smartertools.com/smartermail/business-email-server
5. Their excellent support is worth the price. It's certainly better than the support Microsoft offers. They have a free option for personal use.
6. Courtesy of the Defective by Design campaign: https://www.defectivebydesign.org/amazon-kindle-swindle

7. While some books on Amazon are actually DRM-free, there is no easy way to tell before purchasing as the "Simultaneous Device Usage: Unlimited" tag is a misnomer. It's difficult to obtain usable files even when the book is DRM-free.

Chapter 06: Audiobook Production on Linux

You can use Linux for the complete production of an audiobook, and this chapter guides you through each step of the process. I've used this process for the production of several audiobooks.

However, my advice to you is: do not narrate your own audiobook unless you know what you're getting into. It's a lot of work, and a professional narrator will do a good job. It's worth the money to save the time and effort of doing it yourself. They will also do the engineering for you, which can be a chore to get right.

That being said, I and many others love listening to audiobooks narrated by the author themselves. If you're aware of the work ahead and still want to do it yourself, read on.

Record With Audacity

Audacity is the way to go for recording your audiobook. There's no better free software option on Linux, and there is even a plugin available that you can use to ensure your files meet ACX standards.

Since Audacity 3.0 and significant investment from Muse Group, Audacity has seen significant development. The new non-destructive features have made it a lot easier to work with and make experimentation easier.

ACX stands for "Audiobook Creation eXchange", a platform owned by Amazon and used for submitting your audiobook to Audible, Amazon's audiobook store. Even if you don't want to submit your audiobook to Audible, you should pay attention to the standards anyway, as they are similar for every audiobook store and good guidelines in any case: https://help.acx.com/s/article/what-are-the-acx-audio-submission-requirements

The ACX Check plugin is available here: https://plugins.audacityteam.org/analyzers/analysis-plugins#acx-check

This plugin lets you check your files to see if they meet the standards, and if they don't, you can adjust the file accordingly.

To help meet the standards, you will need to make use of these effects:

- **Noise Reduction:** For removing background noise. You don't want to remove all of it, but you don't want any noise louder than -60dB.
- **Compressor:** For reducing dynamic range, which refers to big spikes in the waveform that indicate a sudden change in volume. You will want to do this before you apply Loudness Normalization, as otherwise the loud parts will be significantly louder than the quieter parts. In most cases, you want the dynamic range to be smaller; you don't want listeners to be constantly adjusting the volume to listen to your audiobook.
- **Loudness Normalization:** For making sure the overall file specifically meets the loudness requirements you set. This is the last effect you want to use, after you're done processing the file, as each effect will adjust the overall volume slightly.

Preparing Your Files

You should export each chapter as an .mp3 file at 192kbps constant bitrate (CBR). I recommend using all Mono for each chapter.

You will usually be asked to submit each chapter as a separate file, but if you're distributing your audiobook directly, you'll also want a single .mp3 file.

Creating a Combined .mp3 File

To get a combined file, you first need to install ffmpeg.

You can get a list of all the audio files in the directory by running this command:

```
ls *.mp3 | tr '\n' '|' | less
```

Copy the output to a text file and remove the files you don't want to be part of the combined file. Then use the resulting output as an argument for the following command, like so:

```
ffmpeg -i "concat:01 audio file.mp3|02 audio file.mp3|03 audio
file.mp3" -acodec
copy final-combined-file.mp3
```

In a minute or so, you'll have a combined .mp3 file containing your entire audiobook.

Creating an .m4b File

If you're distributing your own audiobook, you definitely want an .m4b file. This is a file format specifically designed for audiobooks. It understands the concept of chapters and can include a cover. Users can import this file right into their favourite audiobook program and all of the chapters plus the audiobook cover will be sucked right in.

Creating .m4b files is a little tricky on Linux as there are only a few tools out there you can use to accomplish this.

Andreas Fuhrich has developed two tools for audiobook mastering, tagging, and manipulation. They're the best tools to use for audiobook production on Linux in 2025.

The first is m4b-tool, which is the older but mature tool which will eventually be replaced by tone.

You can download both great tools from Andreas' Github repositories:

- https://github.com/sandreas/m4b-tool
- https://github.com/sandreas/tone

There are executables available on the Releases page that you can simply download and run after installing the right dependencies.

m4b-tool can create an m4b file from a folder of audio files and optionally add metadata, including a cover, description, title, narrated by tag, etc.

Here's how you can use it—first, copy all your audiobook chapters and your cover file to a folder, and copy the description into a description.txt file.

Then, add the chapter Title and Artist to each track using EasyTAG, which is available from Flathub, or id3v2 if you prefer using the command line. Each track needs to have at least these metadata tags, but more tags can be added. This will ensure that each chapter displays nicely in the user's audiobook program.

The .m4b format can hold several audio codecs, but it most commonly uses AAC. This codec has been around since the late 90s, but has received many revisions since. Like most codecs, there were many patents filed at the time it was standardised. The patents for the earlier profiles have expired, but there are active patents for the later, more advanced profiles.

There exist many profiles for AAC, but in most cases, you will want to use the Low Complexity profile, which is the most compatible. Later profiles may not work on all devices.

With this in mind, run m4b-tool on the directory and select the Low Complexity (LC) profile to encode with:

```
m4b-tool merge "audiobook_dir/" --name="A Guide to Desktop
Linux in 2025" --artist="James North" --writer="James
North" --year=2025 --cover=audiobook_dir/cover.jpg --audio-
profile=aac_lc --output-file "audiobook_dir/audiobook.m4b
```

This will take a few minutes, but eventually spit out a .m4b file. You can test it by importing it into Cozy or VLC.

tone can be used to manipulate the tags for audiobook files after they are created. You can view the tags currently attached to the audiobook with:

```
tone dump input.m4b
```

You can modify tags or add new tags like this:

```
tone tag audiobook.m4b -
```

There are a few tags you may want to add that m4b-tool does not support but tone does, so you'll be switching between the two tools.

You can then create an .mp3 file from the .m4b file, which every device should be able to play:

```
ffmpeg -i audiobook.m4b audiobook.mp3
```

Where to Publish Your Audiobook

I highly recommend publishing widely. I do not recommend making your Audiobook exclusive to Audible. Audible will give you a higher cut of the royalties, but all Audible books are encumbered by DRM, and libraries cannot purchase Audible-exclusive audiobooks.

Audible can afford to offer its one-sided royalty rates (Amazon takes 75% of your royalties for non-exclusives and 60% for exclusives) because they think they're the only game in town.

Audible is not the only game in town. You should consider distributing your audiobook to as many stores as possible; Google Play, Audiobooksnow, Libro.fm, and Apple Books are all good options. You should look into selling direct, too. You can keep all of the royalties and charge a more competitive price by selling direct to your readers. If you chose Audible's exclusive deal, you wouldn't be able to sell direct.

Part 2

State of Desktop Linux

Chapter 07: The Wine Gaming Revolution

The rise of Linux as a gaming platform is the most exciting thing to happen in the desktop Linux space in recent memory. It wasn't a small thing, either; it was a seismic shift in Linux's capabilities.

In 2017, you could get a few Windows games running on Linux with some technical know-how and some patience, but they were unlikely to run very well and it was generally a buggy experience except for the simplest and smallest games.

In 2025, you can click Play on a random game in your Steam library and chances are, it'll work flawlessly—in a few cases, it will run better than it does on Windows. Even if the game developers hadn't spared the slightest thought about their game ever running on Linux.

This is no accident. This is the natural conclusion of a revolution more than 30 years in the making.

This is a result of the Wine Gaming Revolution.

What is Wine?

"Wine" is a project nearly as old as Linux itself; it began in 1993, only two years after Linus Torvalds began work on the Linux kernel. It stands for "Wine Is Not an Emulator" but is rendered as "Wine", not "WINE".

As the name suggests, rather than being an emulator, it is instead a compatibility layer. It stands in-between a Windows application and Linux, taking instructions from the application and translating them to instructions that would make sense coming from a native Linux application.

A Brief History of Getting Windows Games to Work on Linux

The first real attempt at running Windows games specifically on Linux, as opposed to just generic Windows applications, was by a company called TransGaming Technologies. This company was established in 2001 by Gavriel State, who was formerly head of the Linux product division at Corel. This came off the heels of Corel selling their Corel Linux distribution and winding down their investment in Wine following a $135 million investment from Microsoft.

The company's first and most well-known product was WineX, which took Wine's codebase and made it proprietary. At the time, Wine was available under the X11 license, which permitted a move like this. Wine had very limited support for DirectX, the then-new graphics/multimedia API by Microsoft. Many Windows games were making use of Direct3D instead of OpenGL, which had come before. Direct3D did not support Linux like OpenGL did, so this was yet another barrier to getting Windows games working on Linux.

TransGaming worked on adding better support for DirectX and DRM to their version of Wine, and the first version launched with support for a grand total of 6 games. This doesn't sound like much, but it laid the groundwork for a decade of further development.

In 2002, the primary Wine developers and companies involved in sponsoring Wine development made the decision to relicense the software under the Lesser General Public License (LGPL) to stop companies like TransGaming from profiting from their contributions without giving anything back. The scope of the project—translating a large portion of the Windows API to get tens of thousands of applications to work on Linux—was so large that if every company worked at this alone, it would be difficult to make a decent amount of headway, and ultimately, compatibility as a whole would be held back. There was nothing to lose from stopping companies from making off with the community's sources and not sharing their improvements.

This was, in fact, exactly what TransGaming was doing. While TransGaming made their codebase publicly available, they did not do so under a license that would allow anyone to contribute the changes back to Wine proper, lest it cut into their profits—who would pay for WineX if they could just use Wine for free? The public codebase was frequently out-of-date and so was not reflective of the capabilities of the paid application.

Since 2002, TransGaming could no longer take any code from Wine, and needed to fund all of the development themselves. In 2004, WineX was renamed to Cedega with the 4.0 release, and would retain that name for the rest of its development.

TransGaming had started working with game developers like EA to ensure their DRM software worked through Cedega. This was great validation for the product, but this part of the source code was never included in the public codebase—possibly because the code that makes their DRM software work is not something most game developers wanted publicly available, or because TransGaming only wanted paying users to be able to play DRM-encumbered games, as a form of upsell.

By 2007, TransGaming had stopped actively developing their Cedega product, as they were more focused on Cider, their product for running Windows games on Macs. Cedega customers were not happy about this, and many publicly stated they were cancelling their subscriptions.

In 2008, TransGaming combined Cider and Cedega into the same product and codebase, and Linux users started getting updates again, but this didn't stop the company from bleeding users. This was the same year the Wine project finally released version 1.0, 15 years after the project began. By this point, many of the features in Cedega were now available in Wine and it was competitive in terms of game compatibility in spite of TransGaming making sure none of their work ever made it back to Wine. It was becoming clear to users that Cedega had lost the edge it once had.

2008 was also the year CodeWeavers launched CrossOver Games, a Wine-based compatibility program for running Windows games on Mac and Linux. CodeWeavers have been around since 1996, initially focused on running Microsoft Office and other office software on Linux. The company employs many of the Wine developers, including the lead developer, and has hosted the WineHQ website for more than 20 years.

While the CrossOver product is proprietary, unlike Cedega, any changes to Wine are released under the LGPL license and most eventually make it back to Wine proper, improving it for everybody. The only proprietary part of the product is the graphical interface.

The bet on copyleft licensing by the Wine Project was paying off just a few years later. The Windows translation layer that the community and companies like CodeWeavers worked on together now worked about as well with games as it did for generic applications, which you couldn't say for Cedega.

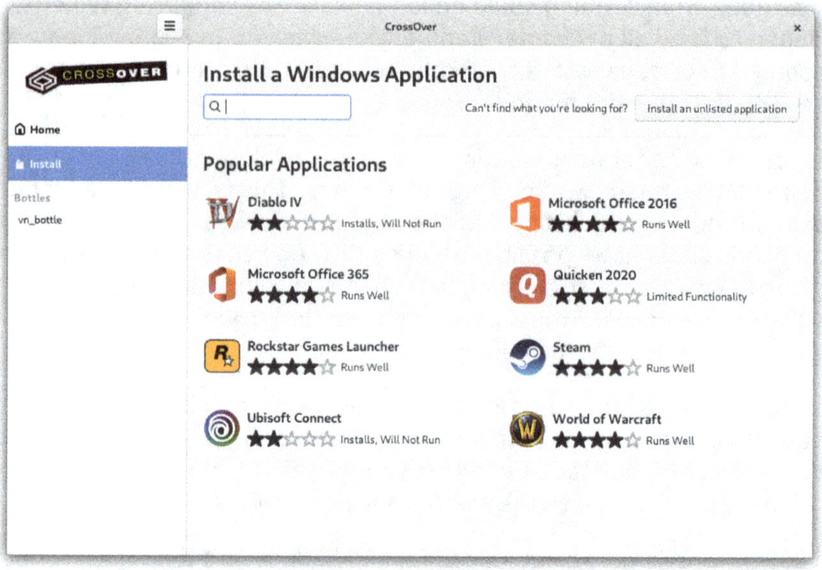

A screenshot of CrossOver 22 from 2022, the latest Full CrossOver version I own.

Looking back, it seemed like a concerted effort to knock Cedega out of the market—if you didn't want to pay money to get games running on Linux, you could just use Wine; if you wanted the best experience possible, CrossOver was a paid solution with a nice graphical interface where your money went to making Wine better for everybody. Why would you pay for Cedega, which in many's view had leeched off the Wine codebase to turn a profit while making sure no one else got any benefit?

It was clear the walls were closing in on Cedega. In 2011, the Cedega product was discontinued along with the codebase, and TransGaming was acquired by NVIDIA in 2015. TransGaming is now a real estate company, having left the technology industry entirely.

TransGaming has left only a legacy of questionable merit behind them. They helped many Linux users play Windows games on their preferred operating system, but because they were working alone and refused to share their work, it took years for the Wine project to develop similar capabilities. Still, there was a time when Cedega was the only solution available for playing the games you wanted to play on Linux, and some Linux users found enough value in that to pay for it. That has to be worth something, at least.

In 2012, CodeWeavers combined all of their CrossOver products into a single product, which meant the end of the dedicated CrossOver Games product. The improvements made to get games running on Linux were still there, but the main focus at this point was on running the Steam client on Linux, which was a window to thousands of games.

Full Steam Ahead

In 2012, Windows 8 was released, and the Windows Store came with it. The existence of the Windows Store was a rather terrifying prospect for a certain company. Gabe Newell, CEO of Valve Software, was concerned that Microsoft could restrict installation of software entirely to the Windows Store under the veil of security, claiming that they only allow sandboxed software on Windows.

By forcing all Windows users to go through the Windows Store, Microsoft gains significant leverage over the vendors distributing Windows software. They might take a cut on all Steam sales, for example.

In reality, this has not come to pass except in a limited capacity; some cheap laptops run Windows S, which only allows users to install software from the Microsoft Store (formerly Windows Store). The main Windows operating systems still allow users to install software from anywhere. This could change in the future, however.

Valve saw this and spent the next few years investing in Linux and convincing OEMs to partner up with them for something they called the "Steam Machine". These were computers that ran SteamOS, a Linux-based operating system, and attempted to replicate the console gaming experience.

Valve engaged with developers who had released games on their platform, convincing them to port their games to Linux so customers would be able to play a decent number of games on these machines. They also released the Steam client and all of their games for Linux.

It was a lot of work and was years in the making.

In 2015, the first Steam Machines released, and... they were not very successful for several reasons. One of the reasons for this was the lack of games available. While there were hundreds more native Linux games thanks to Valve's push, this was still far less than what was available for Windows. Valve discontinued the Steam Machines a year later in 2016.

The reality was, most developers had no interest in porting their games to Linux because the market was paltry compared to Windows and even macOS. The poor sales for the Steam Machines did not do much to convince developers otherwise. By the time they were discontinued, less than half a million units were sold. The Steam Machines were ultimately a failure, though they moved gaming on Linux forward significantly by encouraging more ports.

Let's Try This Again...

Valve did not let the awful Steam Machines launch stop them from trying again. They endeavoured to learn from their mistakes with their first Linux product.

In 2016, Valve contacted CodeWeavers and started aggressively funding work on getting games to work on Linux through Wine, and getting them to work 'at speed'. The partnership continues to this day.

In 2018, Philip Rebohle started his groundbreaking work on DXVK, a translation layer from DirectX to Vulkan. Vulkan is the much newer successor to OpenGL which has great performance and feature parity with the DirectX APIs. Valve sponsored Philip the same year he began the project to continue his work on DXVK full-time, and this has paid dividends.

Valve released the first version of Proton in 2018 with support for 27 games, but users were able to run any Steam game through Proton with varying degrees of success. Valve continued to slowly expand their whitelist of games as Proton got better and better.

Proton is a free software compatibility layer based on Wine and several related projects like DXVK. It's essentially Wine with a few friends, but aimed specifically at getting games to work well on Linux rather than general applications.

In 2019, Joshua Ashton's D9VK project was merged with the DXVK project. D9VK had the same goal as the DXVK project, except that it was focused solely on getting Direct3D9 to work on Linux. Valve would soon hire Joshua Ashton to work on DXVK and other Wine projects.

For a few years, Linux users watched Valve fund all of these projects that improved gaming on Linux significantly and wondered, "why?" Valve had already discontinued their Steam Machines, so clearly they were working on some other Linux-based device, but the company gave nothing away until 2021.

That year, Valve unveiled the Steam Deck, a handheld device that ran a new version of SteamOS, the Linux-based operating system that ran on the Steam Machines. People were skeptical at first given what they knew about the Steam Machines, but the Steam Deck released in 2022 and sold millions of units. Years later, it still sits in the top 10 most-sold products on the Steam charts.

Valve had helped solve the "lack of games" problem with Linux by sponsoring the development of Wine and their own Wine-based technologies like VKD3D-Proton.

And so, as Wine and Proton get better, there are fewer and fewer games that don't work on Linux. It's a far cry from where we started in 1993. In 2025, we're at the vanguard of the Wine Gaming Revolution.

But...What About Native Games?

I'm always appreciative when a game developer releases their game for Linux. It means they care about an audience most bigger publishers don't. It's usually smaller, independent developers who release a Linux version.

For many years, this was a great arrangement for people playing games on Linux. Not too long ago, though, with the advent of DXVK and Proton, native became just another option for supporting Linux players, and an option that requires considerably more resources than doing absolutely nothing.

And that changes things. A lot.

The truth is, Proton actually offers a better experience in some cases than Native releases for a few reasons.

Native games break after a while.

If a developer doesn't bundle all of the right versions of libraries the game needs to work, it ends up depending on what's on the user's computer. And in the future, that's going to change as a user continues to update their system over the years. Eventually, the game will break.

I have personally needed to download a newer version of an engine and place it into the directory, or find libraries a game needs, or even delete libraries in the case of one Ren'Py game to get them to work.

Steam ships with a Runtime that is supposed to include all of the right dependencies, so Steam games don't suffer as badly as games from other stores, but there are still issues with older native games even on Steam.

Nowadays, Flatpak offers a thorough way of packaging up all the dependencies your game needs. Dr. Robotnik's Ring Racers uses Flatpak as a distribution method, which guarantees non-breakage even as the underlying system changes in the future. If more developers distributed their game files via a Flatpak bundle or Appimage, this would go a long way toward solving breakage in the future, but these packaging systems are still not very popular for games.

Native doesn't automatically mean better performance or fewer bugs.

Most developers that release native Linux games are relying on an off-the-shelf engine to accomplish this. That's usually Unity or more recently, Godot. Most of these developers do not have the ability or time to start hacking on the engine to improve the Linux experience. It's usually a low priority—especially if the game has been out for a few years.

Here's a case study that demonstrates how imperfect these engines can be:

Arcen Games made the decision to not release a native Linux executable at all, because performance was worse and less stable compared to Proton, and there were flickering bugs not present with Proton. These were inherent limitations of the Unity engine that couldn't be fixed.

Proton offered a categorically better experience because the DXVK component was more complete than Unity and wrote better-performing instructions. Proton is now so good that it is more performant than commercial game engines.[1]

A native release doesn't guarantee support.

Just because a developer sells a native release does not guarantee they will support it forever. For example, Rocket League originally sold both Linux and macOS versions starting in 2016, and discontinued them in 2020.[2]

A developer might still offer a native Linux release that is broken, and not get around to fixing it even after being informed of it. Chances are, there's a way to get it working, and Linux players are known for their ingenuity. It's surprising how many developers expect Linux players to fix the problem themselves.

Compare this to Proton, which Valve is actively supporting for all Steam games. They are often quicker to fix issues with games than the developers themselves.

A promise of a native release doesn't guarantee a native release.

There's a precedent for developers crowdfunding their games with the promise of a native Linux and macOS release and never delivering either because it turns out to be too hard, costs more money than they thought it would, they can't figure out how to get the DRM to work, or any number of reasons.

Here's a brief history of crowdfunding campaigns and broken promises:

- Stainless Games launched a crowdfunding campaign for *Carmageddon: Reincarnation* in 2012 and reached their goal of $400,000 within 10 days. They announced a stretch goal of $600,000, which came with the promise of macOS and Linux versions of the game. Stainless Games promised that macOS and Linux versions were still coming in 2016, and reiterated this promise in 2018. The game has yet to come to either platform.
- Warhorse Studios launched a crowdfunding campaign for *Kingdom Come: Deliverance* in 2014 with the promise of a macOS and Linux release in 2016, which would have been the first CryEngine game on Linux. In 2015, the studio announced the Linux release would be pushed back. The same year, CryTek announced CryEngine would come to Linux (this promise was actually fulfilled). The next year, Warhorse Studios cancelled both their macOS and Linux ports.
- Nightdive Studios launched a crowdfunding campaign for a *System Shock* reboot in 2016, with macOS and Linux versions as a stretch goal, which was reached. In 2018, Nightdive paused development, but the game was eventually released in 2023. On Windows and console platforms. In 2024, Nightdive Studios announced that both macOS and Linux ports were cancelled with this sentence: *"Unfortunately no, plans for MacOS and Linux releases of System Shock have been shelved."*
- Most recently, a crowdfunding campaign for a game called CONSCRIPT in 2020 was funded with promises for macOS and Linux versions. In 2024, both ports were cancelled, but the developer did something very rare: they refunded any backers who funded the campaign expecting a macOS or Linux version if they contacted the developer.

This is in no way a comprehensive accounting of successful crowdfunding campaigns where the developer failed to deliver a Linux version. I've only mentioned a few to make my point. Unless the developer has a proven track record, you should not assume they will honour their promise of a native Linux version.

GamingOnLinux (GOL) has a database which tracks crowdfunding campaigns that promise Linux builds and the outcome: h*ttps://www.gamingonlinux.com/crowdfunders/*

This database hasn't been updated in some time, so is missing the latest few years of crowdfunded games. Of the 437 finished games, 55 failed to deliver a Linux build, which is a 13% failure rate. This isn't awful, but these stats are enough to make you think twice about a developer's promise to release a native Linux build.

With Wine and Proton, it doesn't matter whether a developer fulfills their promise of a native release or not; chances are, it will work anyway. With or without your money funding development. You can't "cancel" the game from working in Wine or Proton except with Anti-Cheat. It's the ultimate hack. It's likely part of the reason GOL hasn't updated their Crowdfunders database in some time.

So, Native Games Aren't Worth it Anymore?

Not all Native releases are bad! Some are really good, with great support, like Factorio.[3] That being said, if a game is affected by one or more of the above issues, Proton is a better option. But Proton isn't perfect. Not every feature has been implemented, and those that are may not be correctly implemented. So you'll run into bugs that impact performance or cause crashes. It's nice to have a native version as a backup option.

According to Boiling Steam, the number of new native ports since the advent of the Steam Deck has remained largely the same instead of trending sharply down.[4]

The biggest outcome of so many Windows games working so well on Linux with Proton is that Linux players have much higher standards for Linux ports now. This is not a bad thing. It means gaming on Linux is much better now than it was in the years previous, and we can expect to be treated like any other customer, rather than be satisfied with the few alms bestowed upon us, in whatever condition they are given.

The Anti-Cheat Problem

There's just...one problem. While Proton works with pretty much every form of DRM games use on Steam, the same is not true for anti-cheat.

Players have been cheating in video games for a very long time. When someone cheats in a singleplayer game by using Cheat Engine to shuffle memory around, it's no big deal. They bought the game, and they're only ruining their own experience with it.

The same is not true for multiplayer games.

When a player gives themselves the ability to see through walls, or get instant headshots without aiming, that ruins the experience for other players. In a skill-based game, these are unfair advantages that suck the fun out of the game for everyone who isn't cheating.

Historically, players hosted their own servers for PC games, and when they found out someone was cheating, they would just ban that player from their server. That was all there was to it.

Later on, game developers like Valve created software called "anti-cheat" that would be deployed on the server which would detect when players are cheating and punish them accordingly.

Sometime in the last decade, user-owned servers have gone away completely in most games, replaced by the developer's own servers. Anti-cheat software has also moved from the server to the client. As it turns out, there are some things you just can't detect easily unless the software is running on the player's computer. And this software needs to run with very high privileges so a technical user who wants to cheat can't bypass it easily.

Most anti-cheat software today runs in kernel space. There are a few problems with this when it comes to playing these games through Wine. The first problem is that Wine runs in user space without many privileges, so it can't tell what's going on in the kernel. The second problem is that it's so easy for anyone on Linux to recompile their kernel to work around the anti-cheat driver because it's all free software.

While anti-cheat software does exist for Linux, it usually runs in user space. It's not as strong as the anti-cheat software companies push on their Windows players.

In 2022, two very popular anti-cheat products, Easy Anti Cheat and BattlEye, gained support for running in Proton after some coaxing from Valve. Game developers have the option of enabling this support for Proton by sending their anti-cheat vendors an email, but in practice, only about half of the games that rely on anti-cheat enable Proton support. In 2024, a few games that did support anti-cheat running through Proton for years decided to disable it; notably Apex Legends and GTA V.

Developers like Bungie have released statements saying that they will ban users who attempt to circumvent anti-cheat blocks to run the game on Linux, so altering Wine to circumvent anti-cheat is not a solution.

There does not seem to be a lot of confidence in user space anti-cheat, and most developers don't have the appetite to support Linux players, viewing them as more trouble than they're worth.

About half the games that require anti-cheat work in Proton, and about half the games don't. And it's possible, even likely, that fewer games will support Proton by the end of 2025.

It's not clear what the solution is here. This isn't a problem that can be solved by more aggressive development. It's a market share and economics problem. If Linux had 20% market share instead of 2%, more developers might consider enabling Proton support even if it wasn't as good as the Windows anti-cheat. Or they might invest in server-side anti-cheat that works for all operating systems, but this seems unlikely as the trend has been for anti-cheat to burrow deeper into user's systems.

Valve has acknowledged that anti-cheat is an impediment for playing games on Linux devices, even if you are unlikely to play anything competitive on a handheld device like the Steam Deck, but they haven't revealed a strategy for dealing with the problem. It's hard to see what strategy would work, other than outright bribery. The future of games that require anti-cheat on Linux is uncertain.

---

1. Alternatively, the Unity engine is so bad that DXVK was easily able to surpass it as Unity has not put much effort into their Linux building process. Either way, the conclusion is the same: Proton is better.
2. Psyonix offered full refunds to all macOS and Linux owners of Rocket League after discontinuing them, which was the right thing to do.
3. Factorio went to great lengths to make their native port great: https://factorio.com/blog/post/fff-408
4. What Happened to the Native Linux Zealots?: https://boilingsteam.com/what-happened-to-the-native-linux-zealots/index.html

Chapter 08: Problems That No Longer Exist

"But as we all know, Linux is only free if your time has no value."

—Jamie Zawinski (Netscape Employee #20 and "accidental impetus" for the Mozilla project), 1998

Linux has been around for a few decades now. It has always had a reputation for being difficult to use and a great time suck for those willing to make attempts to "grok" it. That reputation is less and less deserved today, but our standards are higher today.

Nonetheless, I think it would do us all a great deal of good to think back on some of the horrible problems that plagued the people before us and breathe a collective sigh of relief that we'll never need to think about them again.

Manually Configuring Your X Server

Imagine you've just completed a fresh install of a Linux distribution in the '90s. It's likely you were dumped into a TTY with a message that tersely informs you there is no valid XFree86 server configuration file.

Yes, you needed to configure your X server before you could get a graphical session running back in the day. There were two widespread wizard-based methods to generate such a configuration file.

The first choice was XF86Setup, which was a graphical program designed to run on as many displays as possible. You needed to select your hardware, and then it would generate a configuration file and attempt to start up the X server.

If XF86Setup failed, you could try the text-based ConfigX86, which would require you to answer a number of questions to auto-generate a configuration file for XFree86.

If both of those tools failed (or your distribution hasn't provided them), you're on your own. Best get reading the man pages to figure out the syntax to write the file yourself.

With the rise of X.org and sane autoconfiguration, you'll never need to touch the X configuration file again unless you really want to.

Perils of Winmodems

In the '90s and early 2000s, people connected to the public internet using dial-up, which relied on the phone line to call up their ISP. The modem sat in the middle, connecting to the computer to the phone line.

There were two types of modems; the hardware modem, which contained all of the circuitry and firmware necessary to perform its duties; and the softmodem (or realistically, the winmodem), which delegated most of its processing to the user's computer and operating system. They were called "winmodems" because they relied on Microsoft Windows drivers to perform their duties.

The majority of "winmodems" did not have drivers for Linux, so Linux users with these types of modems couldn't get online. There were efforts like linmodems to reverse engineer the drivers, but if that didn't work, you'd need to buy a new modem ("this time, a real modem", you might declare).

Most people are not using dial-up today—though some rural areas apparently still rely on it—so winmodems are a thing of the distant past for most of us.

No Wi-Fi Drivers!

In the 2000s and even into the 2010s, chances were good that your Wi-Fi wouldn't work. This is particularly annoying for laptops, because if there wasn't a driver out there that just hadn't made it into the kernel yet, you needed to buy a wireless adapter the kernel did support and have it always plugged in.

If you had a Broadcom chipset, that was a particularly bad case. They're fairly widespread and all of their drivers were proprietary at one point. To get your Wi-Fi working, you would need to connect an ethernet cable or use another computer to get them downloaded, then compile them from source with your kernel. Then, hope it doesn't break when you update the kernel.

Nowadays, Broadcom has created free software drivers that have made it into the kernel, so even most broadcom chipsets will work out of the box. It's a similar case for Realtek and other wireless chipset manufacturers.

It's not entirely a thing of the past, as you still get the odd laptop with an unsupported chipset (some of the last Intel Macbooks, for example), but in 2025, the kernel's support for wireless chipsets is good.

The Capricious Flash Behemoth

Macromedia Flash had been around in some form since at least 1996, and by the early 2000s, it was everywhere. The rise of sites like Newgrounds and Miniclip that hosted user-created Flash games and animations form the bedrock of childhood memories for many in my generation and the previous generation.

There was only one problem… Flash Player didn't support Linux. Well, not at first. In 1999, Macromedia released Flash Player support for Linux (along with Solaris and IRIX, SGI's operating system).[1]

Linux support for the Flash authoring software never materialised, however, so no one on Linux could create Flash animations and games. Aside from that, all was good for a few years. After the acquisition by Adobe, Linux releases of the new Flash Player were delayed for some time, but eventually they would come out. In 2008, Adobe even released Flash Player 10 on the same day as the rest of their supported platforms, so things were looking up.

But in 2012, Adobe decided to stop supporting Linux and left it up to Google to support Chrome users with their Pepper API replacement for Flash.[2] That was only for Google Chrome, though; Firefox didn't have such a replacement. Following this, Adobe also discontinued Acrobat Reader for Linux in 2013, though this carried considerably less gravity, as most developers have not found it difficult to design a better PDF reader than Acrobat.

In the wake of this, users might instead try Gnash, which was a free software Flash player stewarded by the GNU Project that was compatible with a subset of Flash's file formats.

In a strange backtrack, Adobe released a new Linux version of Flash Player 24 in 2016. The timing was even stranger. At this point, Flash was becoming a thing of the past. Browsers were even deprecating it. Adobe would continue support for Linux for another 5 years until it went extinct entirely.

Silverlight never supported Linux officially, but then that was no surprise. Quite a number of sites made use of Silverlight, which made some of the web inaccessible to Linux users. This was particularly felt with banking websites that decided to depend on Silverlight.

I would be remiss not to mention Moonlight, which was a free software implementation of Silverlight by the Mono Project specifically for Linux.[3] The first release was in 2009, but they were forced to abandon it in 2011. It never supported DRM due to Microsoft not being willing to license their PlayReady DRM to Moonlight. Suffice to say, this was not a particularly reliable or long-lived alternative to Silverlight for Linux users.

Fortunately, Silverlight is also no more.

In 2025, the web is wide open to Linux users. Websites might still block Linux users based on their User Agent, but this is trivial to circumvent. Even streaming sites like Netflix and Binge support Linux with their DRM, though they generally don't let you stream above 720p video quality. But that's the worst you can say about the web for Linux.

It took us decades to get here, but the web browser and the web platform itself are now the most robust parts of the Linux Desktop.

Printer Problems

Thankfully, in the modern day, no one ever has trouble setting up—

Sorry, what was that? Both GNOME and KDE's printer settings fail to connect to it with a vague error? Even HP's dedicated graphical program, built specifically for Linux (hplip), doesn't work properly, and they don't provide any drivers on their website? Well, at least if you know the IP address of the printer, you can set it up via IPP using the CUPS web interface at `localhost:631` and find the driver for your model under `/usr/share/ppd`.

Oh well. Some things never change.

---

1. MACROMEDIA INTRODUCES FREE FLASH PLAYERS FOR LINUX, SOLARIS, IRIX USERS., Sept 6, 1999: https://web.archive.org/web/20070520080719/http://www.allbusiness.com/technology/computer-software/300738-1.html
2. Adobe Abandons Flash on Linux, February 2012: https://www.omgubuntu.co.uk/2012/02/adobe-adandons-flash-on-linux
3. The Moonlight repository on Github: https://github.com/mono/moon

Chapter 09: Exploring Different Linux Distributions

There's a common refrain that your choice of distribution doesn't really matter, and I once thought so too. I don't think so anymore.

Depending on the distribution you're using, your day-to-day experience will be very different.

I know exactly what I want from a Linux distribution, and while nothing is quite there yet, there are two distributions that are pretty close already. There are also distributions I would never consider using or never consider using again.

These are my thoughts on different Linux distributions. You're likely to have a very different opinion, but I think you'll find it valuable to learn about a few other distributions than the ones I recommend in Chapter 3, even if it is through my eyes.

Rating Scale

1-5 ⭐; higher is better.

Ubuntu

Rating: ⭐⭐

Ubuntu was my first Linux distribution. I thought it was visually appealing and it wasn't too hard to adapt to, coming from a Windows/macOS background. The design captured me the first time I saw it. It looked like a system I wanted to use.

While I like Ubuntu's look, I don't like the way they've changed the GNOME UX. The only tweaks I make to GNOME are enabling Resize with Secondary-Click, using 10 static workspaces instead of dynamic workspaces, and rebinding a long list of shortcuts. Ubuntu's choices are not for me. I like the default GNOME experience much more and would just end up disabling all of the extensions.

I've always found Ubuntu very buggy. The first time I used it, it would only boot into a black screen a few weeks later, which I now know was the GRUB Rescue screen. I've always had problems installing software in Ubuntu (whether from the Software Center or from apt) because snapd locks the package database and prevents me from installing anything, despite snapd not doing anything at all. The last two times I attempted to install Ubuntu, the installer crashed with an error and failed to install anything at all.

For the month I was able to use Ubuntu, I found it pleasant. I'm interested in revisiting the Ubuntu Core Desktop experience, as I've heard Snaps have become more reliable in the years since, and Snaps have features I'd like to see in Flatpak someday.

I like it as a server distribution, but it's not going back on my desktop.

Pop!_OS

Rating: ★★★★

I used Pop!_OS for a few months well before the announcement of the COSMIC desktop, which is what really makes Pop!_OS interesting. Pop!_OS's brand of GNOME was much nicer to work with as they made so few alterations from the base version of GNOME.

I found it easy-to-use and it was the distribution that really made me love GNOME. The packages are not as new as I'd like, as it is based on the Long-Term Support version of Ubuntu. Despite its base, it was more reliable than Ubuntu in my experience. This may have something to do with Pop!_OS choosing not to use Snap.

I did not like the changes they made with the COSMIC skin over GNOME as I felt they reduced its usability, but I like COSMIC much more as its own desktop environment.

Depending on how quickly COSMIC develops, I may start recommending Pop!_OS to new users instead of Linux Mint.

openSUSE Tumbleweed

Rating: ★★★★

I really like the concept of openSUSE. The installer wizard is the best I've used. More is possible in graphical programs with openSUSE than most other distributions. It's pretty beginner-friendly. It has a lot of the software I want in the repositories, though not everything. The Open Build Service helps fill the gap.

I found, though, that PackageKit would regularly lock up the package manager and I wouldn't be able to install or update packages. This is the same issue I had with Ubuntu, though not quite as bad as it usually resolved itself within a minute.

It ships GNOME without changes, which is fine by me. There's a lot of documentation, but I found some of it lacking because of how dated it was. I was also looking for some more "getting started" docs as opposed to the dense documentation on technical topics.

For some reason, openSUSE enables every single locale by default and doesn't give you an option to configure them, but that's a minor issue.

openSUSE isn't opinionated about non-free software and includes them in their own repository. This is a good thing, because it makes it easy to install the small amount of non-free software I actually need while eschewing the rest.

It also creates snapshots automatically that you can rollback to. This seems useful!

I liked it from the short time I spent with it. But I like other distributions more.

Fedora

Rating: ★★★★

Fedora is the leading desktop distribution in security. It comes with SELinux installed and configured and is one of the few distributions to support secure boot. It has an awesome and knowledgeable community, is backed by Red Hat, and has the best GNOME integration I've seen in a distribution. That is, it's completely vanilla aside from the Software application having the ability to upgrade to the next major version without you needing to touch the terminal.

The distribution is partially rolling. Some system components like Mesa are kept frozen for the current major release, but most packages are kept up-to-date throughout the cycle.

Fedora is a distribution that is so close to being everything I want in a Linux distribution, but it's held back by a few things that aren't strictly its fault.

For instance, it does not have H.264 decoding or encoding support by default. To enable this, you need to explicitly install the OpenH264 package, which allows Fedora to provide basic H.264 decoding and encoding without paying an ungodly sum of money to Via-LA. It is maddening that Fedora does not install this package by default.[1]

This is becoming less of an issue with the advent of NVK and the coming Nova free software drivers, but the proprietary NVIDIA drivers are more difficult to install in Fedora than any other mainstream distribution. You need to install the drivers by adding a third-party repository, RPM Fusion and pasting several commands. The relationship between RPM Fusion and Fedora is also a little...strained, at times.

I like the immutable variants, Silverblue and Kinoite, the most. The problem with those distributions is that they use the Fedora Flatpaks repository by default, which has broken or missing functionality like lack of H.264 support for legal reasons, or are otherwise just older than the Flathub packages. The first thing I do is uninstall all of the Fedora Flatpaks, remove the repository, and install everything I need from Flathub.

Despite all of this, it's a great distribution. It just requires a lot of initial setup work and I can't recommend it to a beginner.

Universal Blue

Rating: ★★★★★

Universal Blue sands down all of the rough edges of Fedora. It comes with H.264 support and proprietary NVIDIA drivers out of the box, removes the Fedora Flatpaks repository entirely and replaces everything with Flathub packages, and it's a joy to use.

It's the best set of immutable distributions available at the end of 2024. It makes the experience viable with the addition of Homebrew and Distrobox by default. I don't care for the devcontainers, though, as setting it up to work with Neovim does not look particularly fun, and I don't use Visual Studio Code.

I will continue to use Aurora on a spare laptop until I'm able to get a better feel for it, but I like it a lot after a few weeks. There are some things I like more on a traditional, mutable distribution, though.

Arch Linux

Rating: ★★★★★

Arch. Its name is the stuff of legends; its legacy long. It's a distribution like any other, but it's not quite like any other.

Arch is Linux. I mean that in the sense that it could just as well be any other Linux distribution, because very little about it is Arch-specific. They do their utmost to ship software with minimal changes from upstream. This means that when there's a problem, it's almost certainly a problem with the software, not Arch-specific.

Arch has been my home for more than 3 years. It's hard to leave because it caters to what I call "the 100% use case" in a way other distributions struggle to. By this, I mean that anything is possible on Arch. Sometimes the simple stuff is a little harder, but the harder stuff is much simpler. It's far more accessible than Gentoo because the learning curve is not high, and it's far easier to get up-to-date software because of the AUR.

The AUR is the greatest equaliser in the Linux world, with Flatpak being the second. Almost anything is available here, and if it isn't, you can package it yourself—easily. It's just a bash script, after all.

You never need to worry about jumping to a new major release because updates happen gradually; it's all rolling.

The documentation is fantastic. So fantastic that it should be the first stop for users of any other Linux distribution, because most of it is not specific to Arch. The community is really helpful, though can be abrasive.

You must secure Arch yourself, as the defaults are not secure. It doesn't even install microcode for your CPU by default. You need to setup desktop environments yourself. This can be easy, but some things can be painful, especially when it comes to NVIDIA.

There is a certain degree of maintenance with Arch you need to keep on top of. Instead of replacing your configurations for system services, Arch will litter the files in the directories, waiting for you to deal with them. If GRUB suddenly breaks one day, you need to fix it. If Arch suddenly decides to start shipping pipewire-media-session and your audio breaks, you need to fix it.

That's annoying, but it's worth it anyway.

Other Distributions

The following is my abbreviated opinions about other distributions:

- **Linux Mint:** it's still reliant on X11; I'm not interested until the Cinnamon Wayland session is stable. The distribution packages are too old for me in any case. I do have a great respect for the amount of work the developers put into making their distribution a nice experience for users, however.
- **UwUntu:** possibly the only reason I might reconsider Ubuntu.

- **Debian:** too old.
- **Trisquel/Parabola/Hyperbola**: too free.
- **Qubes:** too secure.
- **NixOS:** too much work.
- **Gentoo:** way too much work.
- **EndeavourOS/Manjaro/Garuda:** just use Arch.
- **Ubuntu Touch:** it looks cool!
- **ChromeOS:** proprietary, but nothing against it otherwise.

---

1. Fedora is not allowed to compile the OpenH264 package themselves, as then Cisco is no longer responsible for royalty fees; they must use the binary. For that reason, they keep it uninstalled by default despite the fact that OpenH264 is free software and it leads to a very confusing user experience.

Chapter 10: KDE, Now and in the Future

2024 was a big year for KDE, the first real desktop environment for Linux that has been in development since 1996. The year started with the release of Plasma 6 in February, which followed a successful fundraising campaign at the end of 2023.

Plasma 6 defaulted to the new Wayland session for the first time, which now had more capabilities than GNOME's Wayland session and appeared to be just as robust. Plasma also got a new Overview effect that was heavily inspired by GNOME's Activity Overview, developed primarily by Niccolò Venerandi. It's the feature I love most about GNOME, and while it's a little different in Plasma, it makes the environment much more comfortable and productive for me.

Plasma 6 also signalled the start of the Qt6 transition. Many applications were brought over to Qt6 over the course of the year, from Kate to Kdenlive. The Qt6 toolkit has first-class support for the latest Wayland features, but the look has only been iterated on slightly.

Krita's Qt6 transition is still in full swing, as there is considerably more work for them to do than most other KDE applications. Krita heavily patches Qt to work cross-platform, and Qt6's deprecation of ANGLE support has meant that they need to patch it back in themselves. Krita is also not particularly excited by Wayland currently, as there are still some missing features that digital artists depend on, but recognise that they need to port eventually.

One of those features is colour management, which Kwin developer Xaver Hugl spent a lot of time working on this year. The color management protocol is the first step in allowing colour accurate work on Wayland for creative professionals like digital artists and video editors. At the end of 2024, the protocol has been ACKed by the required three parties and only needs a few more implementations before it can be merged.

Once the color management protocol is merged, further work must be done to specify how display response measuring and calibration will work within the protocol. Further, it must also allow for applications like DisplayCAL to pass colour profiles to the compositor to use. Without this, the monitor would need to calibrated elsewhere (on an X11 session, for example) and the profile applied to the monitor.

Another feature necessary for digital artists is extensive drawing tablet configuration options. Plasma 6.1 and 6.2 brought improvements and new features to the drawing tablet settings panel that replicates a subset of the functionality that was present on the X11 session, with more features to come in the future.

It's likely that a lot of this work on colour management and drawing tablets will be done in 2025, and the Wayland session will be nearly feature-complete next to the X11 session with a few new features to boot. There will only be a few items left on the "Plasma/Wayland Known Significant Issues" page once those issues are squared away: https://community.kde.org/Plasma/Wayland_Known_Significant_Issues

KDE's fundraising efforts have been a great success. At the end of 2024, Plasma tried something new. They showed a one-time notification that prompted the user to donate to KDE the first time the user logged into their computer in December.

This resulted in the largest number of donations in a single month KDE has ever received from users. At the end of December, the total donations reached 100,000 Euros.[1] In the previous month, KDE had received only 13,080 Euros in donations, and the total donations for the previous 11 months was about 30,000 Euros less than the donations they received in December.

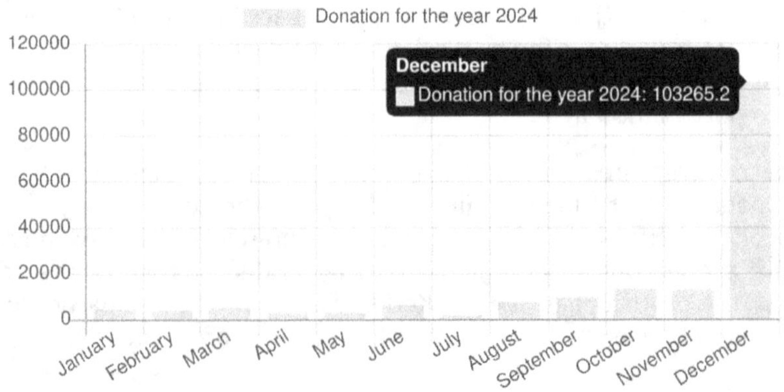

The plan is for the notification to appear once a year in December every year from now. The donation notification only appeared on rolling, up-to-date distributions like Arch Linux, Fedora, and openSUSE Tumbleweed; next year, when stable distributions like Ubuntu have updated to a newer version of KDE, they will also receive the notification.

This is a very healthy development for KDE, which has historically only received large donations from corporations. It's in both user's and KDE's interests to be funded by their users, and this is a great start.

While GNOME has historically been the default desktop environment for most Linux distributions, it was notable that Valve decided to use KDE for their desktop mode with the Steam Deck. Fedora has also named its KDE spin an official Edition, elevating it to the same status as its GNOME edition.

After the KDE 6.x series stabilises, KDE is considering changing to a 6-month release cycle for all of its components.

KDE currently has a 4-month release cycle, which doesn't match up with any Linux distribution's release cycle. Most distributions release a new major version every 6 months, as does GNOME. It's difficult for distributions to schedule around KDE when it has a release cycle that doesn't match up with theirs, so if KDE were to adopt a 6-month release cycle, more distributions might consider defaulting to it instead of GNOME.

I personally don't think this is likely to happen, but it's the first step to making KDE a viable option.

KDE is working on their own immutable distribution, too. They already have KDE Neon, which is based on Ubuntu, but the new KDE Linux will be quite a bit different, as it is based on Arch, and focuses on Flatpaks and Wayland.

Historically, desktop environments like KDE and GNOME don't maintain their own user-facing distributions. They rely on distribution developers like Ubuntu and openSUSE to package up their software and deliver it to users.

The problem with that is they make their own decisions that don't line up with the developer's vision of their desktop environments. KDE Linux, like Neon before it, is meant to be the distribution where you can get KDE right from the source. And it's a very interesting project that integrates all the latest technology for a more reliable, friendly experience.

It's nowhere near ready for release yet, but it'll be interesting to see where it goes in 2025 and beyond.

The future of KDE is bright and interesting.

---

1. Donation numbers: https://kde.org/community/donations/previousdonations/

Chapter 11: GNOME, Now and in the Future

GNOME in 2024

2024 was an interesting year for GNOME. It saw the release of GNOME 46 and GNOME 47. Most of the changes were incremental improvements, but there were a few notable ones.

The Files (Nautilus) application had the most improvements this year, first having the interface completely revamped so it was easier to use, and then having the Open/Save file dialogs completely replaced with a subset of Nautilus' functionality. These dialog windows will show when you need to upload a file in your browser, for example. Previously, the dialog windows were wholly bespoke and had nothing to do with the Nautilus application, making them hard to maintain.

This follows Georges Stavracas' adding thumbnails for images to the previous dialog windows in 2022, finally closing a bug report that had been open since 2002. The new dialog windows offer the same thumbnail functionality, and it means less maintenance because you only need to update Nautilus to update the dialog windows, as it is now the same codebase.

A less-mentioned change is that you can now edit the file path in Nautilus by clicking in the blank space next to the folder path in the URL bar. This is a big usability improvement, especially for new users. Previously, the only way to edit the path was to use the CTRL+L keyboard shortcut.

Nautilus continues to be one of the best file managers available for Linux, and it has only gotten better in 2024.

Another notable change is experimental support for Variable Refresh Rate in GNOME 46, and the addition of accent colours in GNOME 47. You are now able to pick an accent colour from 9 different colours. While the colour is sparsely used in the desktop environment, it's often used for an action button like "Save" or "Open".

This feature comes after several years of discussion regarding how accent colours should work, with some desktop environments completely disagreeing with how much control the user should have over the colour.

The last notable feature is the introduction of completely headless remote desktop sessions in GNOME. This is the first of its kind in the Wayland world. "Headless" refers to the lack of a graphical session. It means that you do not need to already have GNOME up and running before you attempt to login to the computer via RDP. All other Wayland remote access solutions have required that the session already be running for the user before someone is able to connect to it via RDP or VNC.

This is a big change and is thanks to Pascal Nowack's hard work on GNOME Remote Desktop. In GNOME 47, these sessions became persistent; you could disconnect from the session remotely but still leave it running and reconnect to it later.

GNOME is currently the only desktop environment you could deploy on a server that you can expect anyone from any operating system to connect to and use. I have personally setup a server with GNOME that users access via RDP and am impressed with it. It will be interesting to see whether KDE and other desktops catch up, or whether GNOME will continue to improve on its RDP feature.

Funding

At the end of 2023, GNOME was recognised as Public Interest Infrastructure by the Sovereign Tech Fund (now part of the Sovereign Tech Agency), and received 1 million Euros for development on tooling and accessibility features.

This was used for a lot of development in GNOME OS, the distribution developed by GNOME that is built with the latest GNOME software nightly. The operating system received support for features like user home directories being individually encrypted.

The funding was also used to improve Libadwaita, WebkitGTK, and other parts of GNOME's infrastructure which isn't as visible to users. It was also used for development of Variable Refresh Rate.

The 1 million Euros was also directed toward development for accessibility. Matt Campbell received some of this funding to work on Newton, the new accessibility stack for Wayland. There's still a lot of work to go, but considerable progress has been made in this area, which has always been a sore spot for Wayland.

Another important feature the funding was used for was Global Shortcuts, which is also an accessibility feature used by Orca, the screen reader. Dorota (username "dcz") was contracted to work on global shortcuts throughout the year, and made a lot of progress, however, was not able to get the feature merged into GNOME Shell and Control Center this year. Other GNOME developers are continuing to work on getting these features finished.

On May 31st, 2024, the GNOME Foundation announced the GNOME Development Fund. The page[1] described the fund this way:

"The Foundation commits to using at least 80% of the money collected through the Fund for investment into the core GNOME desktop, apps, platform, and development tools, through funding software development, design, usability research, and more. The Fund will be permanent and will run continuously, year-round."

On October 3rd, any text mentioning the Development Fund was removed with no comment. This is a somewhat confusing move especially given the lack of communication from the Foundation, but it may in part be due to funding problems.

Despite receiving 1 million Euros from the Sovereign Tech Fund in late 2023, this funding was targeted and intended to be used for specific types of development projects within a specific timeframe and has now been used up. The GNOME Foundation has been operating at a deficit year-over-year since 2021 and have used up their financial reserves, and so must increase their income to keep spending at the same level.

The financials for non-profit organisations like the GNOME Foundation are complicated; these organisations are not allowed to stockpile money and so must spend most of it within a certain timeframe.

Generally speaking, the amount of software development the GNOME Foundation is responsible for funding is small. Most of the funding is used for event expenses like GUADEC, the yearly GNOME developer conference, and infrastructure expenses, like all of the websites the foundation hosts and the GNOME Gitlab which hosts all of the GNOME Project's source code. The rest of the money is used for running the foundation itself; administration, legal, and accounting staff.

In this context, the disappearance of the Development Fund is disappointing as it would have meant the Foundation would have been directly responsible for funding development of GNOME, which would have marked a big change. Unfortunately, it seems the Foundation has needed to focus on paying staff just to run the Foundation itself at this point in time—however, this is merely speculation, as there has been no official comment on the disappearance of the GNOME Development Fund page.

That being said, the budget for 2025 did mention work on a crowdfunding platform for development fundraising, so the Development Fund may be coming back in a different form in 2025.

Future of GNOME

The GNOME Foundation announced the 2024-2025 budget in October 2024. There were two categories for software development, both externally funded by the Sovereign Tech Fund (STF) and the Endless OS Foundation respectively.

The STF money will be put toward work on the crowdfunding platform for development fundraising, as mentioned above, with a portion of this spent on Flathub's up-and-coming payment system. Flathub is currently a GNOME Foundation project, but it will be brought under its own Foundation over the course of 2025.

The other development category is from the Endless grant, which will be used to develop Parental Controls in GNOME. This makes sense, as Endless OS is targeted toward children in education. Parental Controls includes Digital Wellbeing, which tracks your Screen Time each day and lets you set limits. It also includes "Eyesight Breaks" and "Movement Breaks", which are reminders to take a break on a user-configured Schedule.

I am really looking forward to this, because I currently use Solanum to schedule my own eyesight breaks. It would be awesome to have this directly integrated into the operating system. These are great features for parents, too. These features will likely land in GNOME 48 (due Early 2025) as they are nearly complete.

These features will make Phosh, the GNOME mobile shell, more useful too. While I own a Pinephone, I have not used it for several years due to how bad the battery life is. I don't think the mobile Linux world will be polished to a level that I would consider going back to it in 2025, but I'm glad to see active development on Phosh continues.

One thing I'm curious about is whether the GNOME Project will drop their X11 session in 2025, leaving only their Wayland session. In October 2023, GNOME seemed very eager to drop the X11 session so they could focus all of their resources on their Wayland session.

However, there were still two blocker issues that needed to be resolved before X11 could be dropped. Those were colour management and global shortcut support in GNOME Wayland; these are likely to be implemented sometime in 2025, so we may see the X11 session disappear in GNOME 49 or even GNOME 48, depending on how development goes.

This is no longer as big a deal as it was a few years ago, as most distributions with GNOME already default to Wayland, but a number of users are still using the X11 session because the Wayland session lacks a feature they need. This may no longer be true in 2025.

GNOME is a reliable desktop environment and it seems unlikely that aspect of it will change in 2025, though the GNOME Foundation's future is somewhat uncertain.

---

1. An archived version of the page: https://web.archive.org/web/20241001161655/https://www.gnome.org/donate/

Epilogue: Year of the Linux Desktop?

For at least the past twenty years, tech publications have pondered whether this year will be "The Year of the Linux Desktop". If you're familiar with Betteridge's Law of Headlines1, you'll know none of these articles ended with a particularly optimistic outlook for desktop Linux.

What does that even mean, anyway? What is "The Year of the Linux Desktop"? Everyone seems to interpret it in a different way.

Is it based on market share? Do we need to have more Linux users than Windows users, or more Linux users than macOS users? Does Linux need to dominate, or does it just need to be on-par or almost-on-par with macOS?

There are those who say, "the Year of the Linux Desktop is the year you switched to Linux and never looked back." You can see the reasoning here—who cares if someone else wasn't able to adopt Linux if you were able to? Likewise, who cares if the general public is adopting desktop Linux if you still can't switch because a program you need for work isn't available?

There are some who say, "no, and I hope it will never be The Year of the Linux Desktop!" They believe that for Linux to become a popular option for the desktop, it needs to become commoditised in the same way macOS and Windows are now. They like it as it is now. I think this is all well and good, but I would really like to see a few more professional applications make it over to Linux, and that is only likely to come with more users.

And then there are those who say there will never be a "Year of the Linux Desktop", full stop. For these people, this is a refrain against the idea the general public will ever adopt desktop Linux in meaningful numbers. I must confess that I share the same cynicism.

In its current form, desktop Linux is something you must seek out and actively fight for. To overcome this, we need vendors who will ship Linux on prebuilt computers and laptops like Google did with Android for the phone market.

Google has been attempting to do this with Chromebooks for a few years now, to some success. Chromebooks came a few years after the Netbook craze, which was largely driven by desktop Linux though eventually supplanted by Windows. ChromeOS is Linux, and most of the usual laptop vendors have their own Chromebooks, so Linux is having some limited success in the desktop market.

As mentioned before, there are vendors out there which sell Linux computers online, but few of them are sold in brick-and-mortar stores like Chromebooks are. There is no reason to think this will change in 2025.

However, the handheld gaming market might be dominated by SteamOS in a few years—the Steam Deck is still far more successful than the Windows-based handhelds that came afterward, and Lenovo has just partnered up with Valve for their next handheld; the first handheld other than the Steam Deck to run Linux.2 This may become yet another market Linux dominates in instead of the desktop.

Nowadays, "The Year of the Linux Desktop" is mostly an old joke. No one really takes it seriously. And what does it matter if Desktop Linux isn't a household name, anyway? Desktop Linux is there for those who wish to seek it out. That's how it has always been, and 34 years later, I see no reason why this will change in the near-future.

Even without the benefit of macOS' marketshare, we've brute-forced our way into compatibility with tens of thousands of Windows games with Wine. Who knows what desktop Linux will be capable of 5 years from now? Who knows what the web will be capable of? Maybe those professional applications some of us need to do work will run reliably through Wine—the Affinity Suite is close already.3

If you've read parts of this book and thought, "wow, that sounds kind of painful," on behalf of desktop Linux users everywhere, I appreciate the sympathy.

I've seen people look at how they can do fewer of their day-to-day computing tasks and conclude Linux limits their freedom. Here's how I see it—when you use Linux and a company doesn't let you do something because you lack their approval, you're merely noticing the chains you were wearing the entire time.

This is what I think of when asked what really holds Linux back from being a truly competitive option for the desktop.

It's not money. It's not a lack of developers. It's something we can't control—companies conspiring against their customers. They do it with DRM, they do it with anti-cheat, and they do it with software patents. These are all ways companies seek to control the way you use a product you've paid for, and Linux is incompatible with that.

With Linux, you have real freedom to do whatever you want with your computer. It's something Windows and macOS will never offer you. In a lot of cases, using Linux means seeking out alternatives to products and services you were using before; alternatives that respect your freedom more.

Thankfully, in 2025, there are a lot of great alternatives out there and you need to make far fewer sacrifices than you needed to just ten years ago to use Desktop Linux.

The Year of the Linux Desktop—whatever that means—may never arrive, but we've had a bloody good run of it anyway, I'd say.

---

1. Betteridge's Law states: "Any headline that ends in a question mark can be answered by the word no."
2. Lenovo inviting Valve and Microsoft to their event: https://www.gamingonlinux.com/2024/12/the-upcoming-lenovo-legion-go-s-may-come-with-a-steamos-linux-version/
3. Guide to running Affinity programs on Linux through Wine: https://forum.affinity.serif.com/index.php?/topic/182758-affinity-suite-v204-on-linux-wine/

Resources

So, you're a desktop Linux user now. Where do you go to learn more or just be in the know about what's going on? Lucky for you, I know just the places to go.

While my RSS feed list is long, I've found that only a few sources give me most of the information I want. In this chapter, I bequeath these high-value sources to you.

Text Form

If you prefer reading your news, I recommend these sources:

- This week in GNOME—if you use GNOME, you'll definitely want to hear about the latest developments in GNOME. They post weekly here: thisweek.gnome.org
- This week in Plasma—if you use KDE Plasma, you'll definitely want to hear about the latest developments in KDE. They post weekly here: https://blogs.kde.org/categories/this-week-in-plasma/
- This week in KDE Apps—there is a dedicated blog for all the development happening with KDE Apps, which happens to include a huge number of applications: https://blogs.kde.org/categories/this-week-in-kde-apps/
- gamingonlinux.com—Covers all the latest gaming on Linux news, general PC gaming news, and sometimes general Linux news. It's a great news website that unfortunately had to shut down their forums in 2024 due to UK's new Online Safety Act, which puts the site owner at too much risk to continue running. Thankfully, article comments will remain.

  This is a shame, because the GOL community is one of the friendliest and tight-knit Linux communities on the web that I've had the pleasure of participating in for a few years. Nonetheless, it's still a great site and you can still interact with its great members.

Disclaimer: I have written articles for GamingonLinux in the past under a pseudonym.

- jamesnorth.net/blog—my personal blog. I don't publish regularly, but I like writing guides on all kinds of subjects. I'm particularly proud of my Virt-Manager article that explains how to setup Windows virtual machines from start-to-finish. I wish I had that article when I was figuring it out myself.
- lwn.net—mostly covers server Linux stuff, but occasionally looks at desktop Linux. The long-form desktop Linux articles are very high-quality, so LWN is worth the subscription just for that.

Video Form

I've watched thousands of videos from Linux video creators over the years, but I'll keep my recommendation list down to just three for two specific types of content:

- **The Linux Experiment**: This channel is hosted by Nick, and has a weekly show called "Linux Open Source News", which covers all the notable events that occurred in the past week. He also posts one-off videos on various desktop Linux subjects. Sometimes it's a tutorial series, a think-piece about packaging, or a review of a new Linux computer. I don't think there's a better video creator to start with.

  You can find his videos on YouTube and on tilvids.com, a PeerTube instance.

- **Brodie Robertson:** An Aussie who posts 6 times a week, and often covers obscure, highly technical content like the wayland-protocols merge request discussions in a way most people can understand. He doesn't miss much. You could watch Brodie Roberston's videos and nothing else and get a great understanding of what's going on in the desktop Linux world.

- **Tech Over Tea:** This is a video podcast Brodie Robertson hosts regularly. It is some of the best Linux content on the web because he speaks directly with developers and users you wouldn't usually hear from, and the episodes are about 2 hours long. It's a great show for new users and veterans. You probably won't be interested in most of the episodes because the topics are so broad, but the ones that do catch your eye are gold. There is, however, no tea in these episodes.

If you want more video content, you should seek it out—it's not hard to find. However, I've found that these two creators cover everything you need to know about desktop Linux quite well.

Recommended RSS Feed Readers

You can plug all of these sources into your RSS feed reader instead of checking the websites periodically for updates, and I highly recommend you do so.

I recommend these feed readers:

- **Newsflash:** a beautiful graphical RSS feed reader that is easy to use. You can install it from Flathub.
- **Newsraft:** an intentionally simple, fast terminal-based RSS feed reader with a simple configuration file. It's a little tricky to compile the dependencies for this program on most distributions, so you might try out Newsboat instead, which is in most distribution's repositories.

About The Author, James North

James North started using Linux on the desktop in 2020, primarily out of curiosity. The technology was starkly different to the Microsoft Windows system James was familiar with, but so was the culture and philosophy. Somewhere along the way, it became about far more than just Linux. You can't learn much about Linux without also learning a lot about computing and free software in general.

5 years later, James is still using Linux on the desktop.

James is the resident system administrator and lead UI designer at Evolvepreneur. All the servers, as you would expect, run on Linux.

James maintains a weblog at jamesnorth.net

James hosts a wiki about visual novels at wiki.vncompat.org

James' free software tools, including mkshousetsu and feedhook, can be found on Codeberg: https://codeberg.org/gnuisance

Creative Commons Attribution-NonCommercial-ShareAlike 4.0 International License

Creative Commons Corporation ("Creative Commons") is not a law firm and does not provide legal services or legal advice. Distribution of Creative Commons public licenses does not create a lawyer-client or other relationship. Creative Commons makes its licenses and related information available on an "as-is" basis. Creative Commons gives no warranties regarding its licenses, any material licensed under their terms and conditions, or any related information. Creative Commons disclaims all liability for damages resulting from their use to the fullest extent possible.

Using Creative Commons Public Licenses

Creative Commons public licenses provide a standard set of terms and conditions that creators and other rights holders may use to share original works of authorship and other material subject to copyright and certain other rights specified in the public license below. The following considerations are for informational purposes only, are not exhaustive, and do not form part of our licenses.

- Considerations for licensors: Our public licenses are intended for use by those authorized to give the public permission to use material in ways otherwise restricted by copyright and certain other rights. Our licenses are irrevocable. Licensors should read and understand the terms and conditions of the license they choose before applying it. Licensors should also secure all rights necessary before applying our licenses so that the public can reuse the material as expected. Licensors should clearly mark any material not subject to the license. This includes other CC- licensed material, or material used under an exception or limitation to copyright. More considerations for licensors: wiki.creativecommons.org/Considerations_for_licensors
- Considerations for the public: By using one of our public licenses, a licensor grants the public permission to use the licensed material

d. Copyright and Similar Rights means copyright and/or similar rights closely related to copyright including, without limitation, performance, broadcast, sound recording, and Sui Generis Database Rights, without regard to how the rights are labeled or categorized. For purposes of this Public License, the rights specified in Section 2(b)(1)-(2) are not Copyright and Similar Rights.

e. Effective Technological Measures means those measures that, in the absence of proper authority, may not be circumvented under laws fulfilling obligations under Article 11 of the WIPO Copyright Treaty adopted on December 20, 1996, and/or similar international agreements.

f. Exceptions and Limitations means fair use, fair dealing, and/or any other exception or limitation to Copyright and Similar Rights that applies to Your use of the Licensed Material.

g. License Elements means the license attributes listed in the name of a Creative Commons Public License. The License Elements of this Public License are Attribution, NonCommercial, and ShareAlike.

h. Licensed Material means the artistic or literary work, database, or other material to which the Licensor applied this Public License.

i. Licensed Rights means the rights granted to You subject to the terms and conditions of this Public License, which are limited to all Copyright and Similar Rights that apply to Your use of the Licensed Material and that the Licensor has authority to license.

j. Licensor means the individual(s) or entity(ies) granting rights under this Public License.

k. NonCommercial means not primarily intended for or directed towards commercial advantage or monetary compensation. For purposes of this Public License, the exchange of the Licensed Material for other material subject to Copyright and Similar Rights by digital file-sharing or similar means is NonCommercial provided there is no payment of monetary compensation in connection with the exchange.

l. Share means to provide material to the public by any means or process that requires permission under the Licensed Rights, such as reproduction, public display, public performance, distribution, dissemination, communication, or importation, and to make material available to the public including in ways that members of the public may access the material from a place and at a time individually chosen by them.

m. Sui Generis Database Rights means rights other than copyright resulting from Directive 96/9/EC of the European Parliament and of the Council of 11 March 1996 on the legal protection of databases, as amended and/or succeeded, as well as other essentially equivalent rights anywhere in the world.

n. You means the individual or entity exercising the Licensed Rights under this Public License. Your has a corresponding meaning.

Section 2 – Scope.

a. License grant.

1. Subject to the terms and conditions of this Public License, the Licensor hereby grants You a worldwide, royalty-free, non-sublicensable, non-exclusive, irrevocable license to exercise the Licensed Rights in the Licensed Material to:

   b. reproduce and Share the Licensed Material, in whole or in part, for NonCommercial purposes only; and

   c. produce, reproduce, and Share Adapted Material for NonCommercial purposes only.

2. Exceptions and Limitations. For the avoidance of doubt, where Exceptions and Limitations apply to Your use, this Public License does not apply, and You do not need to comply with its terms and conditions.

3. Term. The term of this Public License is specified in Section 6(a).

4. Media and formats; technical modifications allowed. The Licensor authorizes You to exercise the Licensed Rights in all media and formats whether now known or hereafter created, and to make technical modifications necessary to do so. The Licensor waives and/or agrees not to assert any right or authority to forbid You from making technical modifications necessary to exercise the Licensed Rights, including technical modifications necessary to circumvent Effective Technological Measures. For purposes of this Public License, simply making modifications authorized by this Section 2(a)

   4. never produces Adapted Material.

5. Downstream recipients.

a. Offer from the Licensor – Licensed Material. Every recipient of the Licensed Material automatically receives an offer from the Licensor to exercise the Licensed Rights under the terms and conditions of this Public License.

b. Additional offer from the Licensor – Adapted Material. Every recipient of Adapted Material from You automatically receives an offer from the Licensor to exercise the Licensed Rights in the Adapted Material under the conditions of the Adapter's License You apply.

c. No downstream restrictions. You may not offer or impose any additional or different terms or conditions on, or apply any Effective Technological Measures to, the Licensed Material if doing so restricts exercise of the Licensed Rights by any recipient of the Licensed Material.

6. No endorsement. Nothing in this Public License constitutes or may be construed as permission to assert or imply that You are, or that Your use of the Licensed Material is, connected with, or sponsored, endorsed, or granted official status by, the Licensor or others designated to receive attribution as provided in Section 3(a)(1)(A)(i).

b. Other rights.

1. Moral rights, such as the right of integrity, are not licensed under this Public License, nor are publicity, privacy, and/or other similar personality rights; however, to the extent possible, the Licensor waives and/or agrees not to assert any such rights held by the Licensor to the limited extent necessary to allow You to exercise the Licensed Rights, but not otherwise.

2. Patent and trademark rights are not licensed under this Public License.

3. To the extent possible, the Licensor waives any right to collect royalties from You for the exercise of the Licensed Rights, whether directly or through a collecting society under any voluntary or waivable statutory or compulsory licensing scheme. In all other cases the Licensor expressly reserves any right to collect such royalties, including when the Licensed Material is used other than for NonCommercial purposes.

Section 3 – License Conditions.

Your exercise of the Licensed Rights is expressly made subject to the following conditions.

a. Attribution.

   1. If You Share the Licensed Material (including in modified form), You must:

      a. retain the following if it is supplied by the Licensor with the Licensed Material:

         i. identification of the creator(s) of the Licensed Material and any others designated to receive attribution, in any reasonable manner requested by the Licensor (including by pseudonym if designated);

         ii. a copyright notice;

         iii. a notice that refers to this Public License;

         iv. a notice that refers to the disclaimer of warranties;

         v. a URI or hyperlink to the Licensed Material to the extent reasonably practicable;

      b. indicate if You modified the Licensed Material and retain an indication of any previous modifications; and

      c. indicate the Licensed Material is licensed under this Public License, and include the text of, or the URI or hyperlink to, this Public License.

   1. You may satisfy the conditions in Section 3(a)(1) in any reasonable manner based on the medium, means, and context in which You Share the Licensed Material. For example, it may be reasonable to satisfy the conditions by providing a URI or hyperlink to a resource that includes the required information.

   2. If requested by the Licensor, You must remove any of the information required by Section 3(a)(1)(A) to the extent reasonably practicable.

b. ShareAlike.

In addition to the conditions in Section 3(a), if You Share Adapted Material You produce, the following conditions also apply.

1. The Adapter's License You apply must be a Creative Commons license with the same License Elements, this version or later, or a BY-NC-SA Compatible License.

2. You must include the text of, or the URI or hyperlink to, the Adapter's License You apply. You may satisfy this condition in any reasonable manner based on the medium, means, and context in which You Share Adapted Material.

3. You may not offer or impose any additional or different terms or conditions on, or apply any Effective Technological Measures to, Adapted Material that restrict exercise of the rights granted under the Adapter's License You apply.

Section 4 – Sui Generis Database Rights.

Where the Licensed Rights include Sui Generis Database Rights that apply to Your use of the Licensed Material:

a. for the avoidance of doubt, Section 2(a)(1) grants You the right to extract, reuse, reproduce, and Share all or a substantial portion of the contents of the database for NonCommercial purposes only;
b. if You include all or a substantial portion of the database contents in a database in which You have Sui Generis Database Rights, then the database in which You have Sui Generis Database Rights (but not its individual contents) is Adapted Material, including for purposes of Section 3(b); and
c. You must comply with the conditions in Section 3(a) if You Share all or a substantial portion of the contents of the database.

For the avoidance of doubt, this Section 4 supplements and does not replace Your obligations under this Public License where the Licensed Rights include other Copyright and Similar Rights.

Section 5 – Disclaimer of Warranties and Limitation of Liability.

a. UNLESS OTHERWISE SEPARATELY UNDERTAKEN BY THE LICENSOR, TO THE EXTENT POSSIBLE, THE LICENSOR OFFERS THE LICENSED MATERIAL AS-IS AND AS-AVAILABLE, AND MAKES NO REPRESENTATIONS OR WARRANTIES OF ANY KIND CONCERNING THE LICENSED MATERIAL, WHETHER EXPRESS, IMPLIED, STATUTORY, OR OTHER. THIS INCLUDES, WITHOUT LIMITATION, WARRANTIES OF TITLE, MERCHANTABILITY, FITNESS FOR A PARTICULAR PURPOSE, NON-INFRINGEMENT, ABSENCE OF LATENT OR OTHER DEFECTS, ACCURACY, OR THE PRESENCE OR ABSENCE OF ERRORS, WHETHER OR NOT KNOWN OR DISCOVERABLE. WHERE DISCLAIMERS OF WARRANTIES ARE NOT ALLOWED IN FULL OR IN PART, THIS DISCLAIMER MAY NOT APPLY TO YOU.

b. TO THE EXTENT POSSIBLE, IN NO EVENT WILL THE LICENSOR BE LIABLE TO YOU ON ANY LEGAL THEORY (INCLUDING, WITHOUT LIMITATION, NEGLIGENCE) OR OTHERWISE FOR ANY DIRECT, SPECIAL, INDIRECT, INCIDENTAL, CONSEQUENTIAL, PUNITIVE, EXEMPLARY, OR OTHER LOSSES, COSTS, EXPENSES, OR DAMAGES ARISING OUT OF THIS PUBLIC LICENSE OR USE OF THE LICENSED MATERIAL, EVEN IF THE LICENSOR HAS BEEN ADVISED OF THE POSSIBILITY OF SUCH LOSSES, COSTS, EXPENSES, OR DAMAGES. WHERE A LIMITATION OF LIABILITY IS NOT ALLOWED IN FULL OR IN PART, THIS LIMITATION MAY NOT APPLY TO YOU.

c. The disclaimer of warranties and limitation of liability provided above shall be interpreted in a manner that, to the extent possible, most closely approximates an absolute disclaimer and waiver of all liability.

Section 6 – Term and Termination.

a. This Public License applies for the term of the Copyright and Similar Rights licensed here. However, if You fail to comply with this Public License, then Your rights under this Public License terminate automatically.

b. Where Your right to use the Licensed Material has terminated under Section 6(a), it reinstates:

    1. automatically as of the date the violation is cured, provided it is cured within 30 days of Your discovery of the violation; or

2. upon express reinstatement by the Licensor.

For the avoidance of doubt, this Section 6(b) does not affect any right the Licensor may have to seek remedies for Your violations of this Public License.

c. For the avoidance of doubt, the Licensor may also offer the Licensed Material under separate terms or conditions or stop distributing the Licensed Material at any time; however, doing so will not terminate this Public License.

d. Sections 1, 5, 6, 7, and 8 survive termination of this Public License.

Section 7 – Other Terms and Conditions.

a. The Licensor shall not be bound by any additional or different terms or conditions communicated by You unless expressly agreed.

b. Any arrangements, understandings, or agreements regarding the Licensed Material not stated herein are separate from and independent of the terms and conditions of this Public License.

Section 8 – Interpretation.

a. For the avoidance of doubt, this Public License does not, and shall not be interpreted to, reduce, limit, restrict, or impose conditions on any use of the Licensed Material that could lawfully be made without permission under this Public License.

b. To the extent possible, if any provision of this Public License is deemed unenforceable, it shall be automatically reformed to the minimum extent necessary to make it enforceable. If the provision cannot be reformed, it shall be severed from this Public License without affecting the enforceability of the remaining terms and conditions.

c. No term or condition of this Public License will be waived and no failure to comply consented to unless expressly agreed to by the Licensor.

d. Nothing in this Public License constitutes or may be interpreted as a limitation upon, or waiver of, any privileges and immunities that apply to the Licensor or You, including from the legal processes of any jurisdiction or authority.

www.ingramcontent.com/pod-product-compliance
Lightning Source LLC
LaVergne TN
LVHW011513200926
848484LV00001B/32
* 9 7 8 1 9 2 3 2 2 3 6 8 4 *